Slimming World

extra easy
express

Slimming
WORLD

touching hearts, changing lives

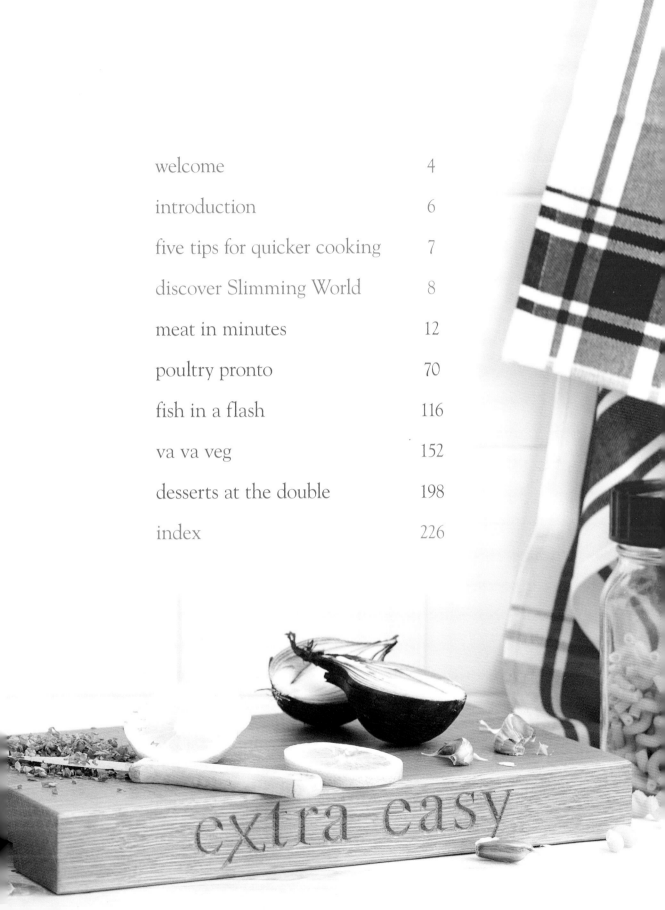

extra easy

a warm
Slimming World
welcome…

…to **Extra Easy Express**, perfect for food lovers who want fabulous, filling meals in a flash!

These days, the one thing everyone's short of is time – and that gets us into all sorts of trouble when we're trying to lose weight. Takeaways, ready meals, grabbing food on the run – they all sabotage our very best efforts to slim. So this book is truly a godsend – it'll help you serve up delicious and slimming meals in minutes. Who wouldn't love that!

Food Optimising – the famous eating plan that lies at the very heart of Slimming World – was born back in 1969 out of my own love of food and a desire to help people lift both the physical and emotional burden of being overweight. Having tried many diets, without lasting success, I concluded that hunger, deprivation and guilt were not the answer. No diet that made me skip meals, cut out my favourite foods, eat separately from my family or curtail my social life was ever going to work for me!

To change my life I needed an easy, flexible way of eating. I needed freedom from the fear of hunger, and freedom from the stress of obsessively counting calories. And I needed the support of fellow slimmers – people who truly understood how it felt to be overweight. Developing Food Optimising, an amazing weight-loss system to liberate slimmers everywhere, and creating a first-class support system to motivate them to bring their dreams to life was my vision all those years ago and it remains to this day.

It seems too good to be true to be able to eat as much as you like of the foods you enjoy and still lose weight, doesn't it? But Food Optimising isn't magic; it's based on scientific research into how our appetite works and how we can satisfy it without gaining weight. At Slimming World we also have a deep understanding of how it feels to have a weight problem. Vitally, we know how to inspire and motivate slimmers every step of the way as they journey towards their own personal target weight.

This genuine understanding is what makes Slimming World groups so special. It's why we're known as the club that cares. It's why we now have around 12,000 groups in the UK and Ireland – every one run by highly trained and supportive Consultants who have been members themselves and who know exactly what it's like to take that first courageous step towards a slimmer, healthier and happier life. And it's why we offer the very best help and support there is for slimmers out there, anywhere.

Part of that support is giving you, through our books, website and magazine, tons of inspiration to help make your weight loss journey easier. That's why I'm so thrilled to present *Extra Easy Express* – it's bursting with recipes that you'll love to cook, eat and share with family and friends. And it'll mean you spend less time over a hot stove and more time enjoying life. That gets my vote every time!

With warmest wishes from the club with the big heart and from me,

Margaret Miles-Bramwell OBE HonMUniv FRSA
Founder and Chairman

introducing
extra easy
express

At the end of a busy day there's only one thing more welcome than a healthy, filling and delicious meal… and that's a healthy, filling and delicious meal that's ready in a flash!

Making home-cooked meals doesn't have to be a chore and it's the best possible way to keep your weight loss on track. And if you can do it in minutes, so much the better – especially if you have hungry mouths to feed or you want to make the most of your evening.

So we've created *Extra Easy Express* to help you enjoy real food – fast. Every meal is tasty, satisfying and will help speed you to your dream weight… yet all of the recipes take less than 30 minutes to cook, and many are even speedier.

With more than 100 simple dishes to choose from, you can be sure of finding a food fix wherever your appetite leads you. There are quick versions of classic dishes such as beef stew and chicken curry, plus exciting and speedy ideas like all-day breakfast spaghetti and Moroccan lamb. And because every main course is so quick to make, there's time to finish off with one of our divine desserts (if you don't have 10 minutes, our tutti frutti sorbet is ready to scoop in five!).

Every recipe is based on Food Optimising, Slimming World's unique healthy eating plan, which means that you can fill up on everyday foods like meat, chicken, fish, pasta, rice and vegetables to your heart's content and never feel hungry. And we can guarantee your friends and family will love every dish too.

So welcome to *Extra Easy Express*, our amazing collection of quick-cook meals that will help you fill up and lose weight… without the wait!

❄ Recipes marked with this symbol can be frozen.

Ⓥ Recipes suitable for vegetarians have this symbol.

five tips
for quicker cooking

A little bit of planning and a few clever short-cuts can make all the difference when you want to serve up magical meals in minutes. Here are five easy ways to trim the time you spend in the kitchen.

1 Chop on the hop: use the down-time to prepare ingredients

You'll save time by doing most of your chopping while other ingredients are cooking. For example, if you're making a tasty stir-fry with rice, it's usually faster to get the rice on first – then chop your onions, garlic and peppers.

2 Smaller is speedier

Finely chopping or dicing an ingredient takes a little longer but the smaller the pieces are, the faster they cook.

3 Shopping not chopping: buy pre-prepared fresh vegetables

If you love cooking with fresh fruit and vegetables but find peeling and chopping a drag, there is another way! Supermarkets have lots of chopped fruit and veg available in pre-prepared packs so you don't have to lift a finger, including onions, broccoli, pineapple, peppers, carrots and mixed stir-fry vegetables. You'll spend a bit more but save a lot of time and effort.

4 A longer life: use frozen and canned foods too

Frozen and canned foods are just as filling and healthy as the fresh kind and we've used plenty of both in this book. Frozen food is usually slightly quicker to cook than fresh, and canned food is quicker still as it only needs heating through. Another bonus is that both can be stored for ages, giving you a supply of healthy Free Foods to use in your meals. Feel free to switch between fresh, frozen and canned foods but remember to adjust the cooking time if necessary. Choose meat, fish or vegetables that are canned in water or brine to avoid adding Syns.

5 Be kitchen smart

Keeping your kitchen, clean, tidy and organised is a big help when you want to cook fast. Assemble all the ingredients for your recipe, as this avoids searching for things at the back of the cupboard when you need them most. You can also save time by having the bin close by for easy disposal of peel and packaging, and keeping knives sharp for easy slicing.

discover
the Slimming World
experience

A guide to Food Optimising, IMAGE Therapy and Body Magic

At Slimming World we love to eat well. We also know that for most of us there aren't enough hours in the day… so getting food on the table in a flash is always welcome! This indispensable cookbook features more than 100 speedy recipes based on Food Optimising, our revolutionary healthy eating plan. Here's a simple guide to how it works.

Light years ahead

With Food Optimising, you can enjoy fabulous and filling food, treat yourself every day and still lose weight beautifully to reach your dream weight. What's more, it's a healthy way of eating that helps you stay slim and healthy for life.

You might wonder how that's possible! Well, unlike typical 'diets', Food Optimising works in harmony with your natural appetite and love of food. At Slimming World we encourage you to enjoy eating without feeling guilty or deprived, which is so often the damaging result of following faddy diets that are hard to stick to.

Food Optimising is based on the sound scientific principle that to lose weight you have to eat less energy (in the form of calories) than you use. Typical diets aim to restrict your energy intake in various ways, for instance by making you count every calorie, by banning high-calorie foods or imposing restrictions such as not eating different types of food together.

Slimming World couldn't be more different – it's light years ahead, and we're with you all the way, no matter how much weight you have to lose.

Free Foods

Food Optimising is based on the scientific principle of energy density. Put simply, that means choosing foods that are low in energy density, so they're naturally low in calories and also really filling. We call these Free Foods and they are the main reason Food Optimising is so easy and effective. Free Foods take away the fear of hunger, the worry about over-eating and the stress of counting calories that are the downfall of so many unsuccessful slimmers. Eat as much Free Food as you like and as often as you like without ever having to worry about weighing or measuring. Fill up on Free Foods – make meals from them, rely on them and enjoy them day and night to satisfy your hunger! You get the picture that we're really passionate about Free Food!

So what are these magical Free Foods? Amazingly, they're ordinary everyday foods like lean meat and fish, fruit and vegetables, pasta and potatoes – so there's no need to worry about finding them in the supermarket, and certainly no need to buy expensive ready-made meals.

No weighing,
no measuring,
no counting…
no kidding!

Research into the science of appetite, much of which Slimming World has sponsored, shows that protein-rich and carbohydrate-rich foods like lean meat, beans, eggs, fat free dairy products, potatoes, rice and noodles are more satisfying and filling than foods that are high in fat and sugar. Nearly all fruit and vegetables are Free Foods too – they tend to be relatively low in calories for their weight so they're full of filling power as well as valuable vitamins, minerals and fibre. By building meals around the huge range of Free Foods, Food Optimisers naturally reduce their energy intake without feeling hungry or having to count a single calorie – resulting in week after week of amazing meals and steady weight loss that feels almost effortless.

The key to successful Food Optimising is to make Free Foods work for you. You can eat these in unlimited amounts and they'll keep you satisfied, even on your hungriest days. They are the key to long-term success.

Everyday extras

As well as Free Foods, Food Optimising has two other vital elements: Healthy Extras and Syns.

Healthy Extras are nutrient-rich foods that are essential to good health, such as calcium or dietary fibre. They are the next step to success! Each day, Food Optimisers choose measured servings of Healthy Extra foods such as wholemeal bread, cereal, cheese or milk – perfect for a balanced diet and enjoying simple everyday pleasures such as a lunchtime sandwich or cereal for breakfast.

And what about Syns? Syns are the food choices (yes, even more food!) that help to make Food Optimising uniquely enjoyable and easy to stick to. Each day, Slimming World members can choose how to use their daily allocation of Syns – perhaps a bar of chocolate or some biscuits, a creamy sauce with dinner, mayonnaise on a sandwich or a glass of wine – and enjoy them without ever feeling guilty or deprived.

Foods with a Syn value tend to be 'energy-dense', meaning they are high in calories for their weight and easy to overeat – and limiting them means members can balance their diet for optimum weight loss and maximum enjoyment!

Together, Free Foods, Healthy Extras and Syns are an unbeatable combination that makes Food Optimising the most flexible, generous and enjoyable weight loss plan you'll find – and it's so healthy and easy to follow that once they reach target, Slimming World members happily become Food Optimisers for life!

So much choice and variety

One aspect of Slimming World that often surprises new members is that there are no set menus to 'stick to'. It's another reason why Food Optimising is suitable for absolutely everyone: whether you're following a special diet for health or religious reasons, are vegan or vegetarian, or have strong food likes and dislikes (and who doesn't?), there are so many ways to make tasty, filling meals.

At each meal you fill at least a third of your plate with fruit or veg and then enjoy a wide range of Free Foods – such as lean meat, poultry and fish, pasta and potatoes and beans and pulses. Add measured Healthy Extra choices and your Syns for the day and you're up and running to a great weight loss, the Extra Easy way. If you Food Optimise 100% you will lose weight. And with so much choice and variety, you'll never be bored!

When you join a Slimming World group, you'll find that your Consultant and fellow members will be full of inspiration, and there are literally thousands of delicious recipes to try in our books, magazines and online, with every one of them based on tried-and-tested Food Optimising principles.

IMAGE Therapy: support every step of the way

While this delicious collection of recipes gives you a taste of Food Optimising, the complete Slimming World experience offers so much more during your slimming journey. Our warm, practical group support and individual help for members set Slimming World apart as the organisation that really understands and, more importantly, cares deeply about your success.

IMAGE Therapy, which stands for Individual Motivation and Group Experience, is a unique support system, shared by the group yet tailored to meet each individual member's needs.

Each week, every member has the opportunity to celebrate achievements, discuss challenges and share insights and milestones with their Consultant and fellow slimmers in an atmosphere that is completely safe and supportive. Many members say that IMAGE Therapy is not just their favourite part of the Slimming World meeting but the highlight of their week. IMAGE Therapy is based on a deep understanding of the psychology of slimming but it never feels like hard work; it's fun, informative, inspiring and most of all, effective at helping members see their way over obstacles and plot their path to success. The power of IMAGE Therapy is the reason you're much more likely to succeed in a group than trying to 'go it alone'.

Body Magic: getting active at your own pace

Along with Food Optimising and IMAGE Therapy, the third key element of the Slimming World experience is Body Magic – an amazing lifestyle activity programme that helps members boost their weight loss, get fit and stay slim and active for life. As you would expect with Slimming World, Body Magic is all about choices and building active habits at your own pace – NOT about going to the gym or pushing yourself to extremes. Whether you've never exercised before or you're an avid exerciser, Body Magic starts where you are and encourages you to be a bit more active, more often.

Each week, members set their own activity goals and are supported and rewarded at every stage with awards: Bronze, Silver, Gold and Platinum. Any form of activity counts, from brisk walking, running and swimming and formal sports to vigorous household chores or dancing in front of the TV, and the more active you get, the more Body Magic awards you can pick up along the way! Ultimately, the aim is to find activities that you enjoy and can stick to, which is key to making healthy changes that will last a lifetime.

A magic mix

Together, this magic mix of Food Optimising (for people who love to eat!), uplifting and supportive IMAGE Therapy (which sets members up for a fabulous week – every week), and Body Magic (which empowers members to take small steps towards a more active lifestyle) is what makes Slimming World different to anything else out there! It has already helped millions of men and women lose weight and live happily (and healthily) ever after!

We hope you'll love creating the speedy dishes in Extra Easy Express as much as we did, and that they whet your appetite for the whole Slimming World experience. Your journey, your slim new life, really does start here, so come along and join in the fun – we guarantee you'll soon be on the fast track to success!

For details of a warm and friendly group near you, call 0844 897 8000 or visit www.slimmingworld.com

meat in minutes

At Slimming World we just love meat – everything from beautiful beef and luscious lamb to perfect pork. As well as tasting amazing and being fantastically filling, meat can be flash-fried or grilled in no time, making it the fast cook's best friend!

easy
beef stew

serves 4

each serving is:

Free on Extra Easy

Free on Original

8 Syns on Green

low calorie cooking spray

500g lean sirloin steak,
all visible fat removed

2 onions, finely sliced

3 garlic cloves, finely sliced

2 tsp dried oregano

400g can chopped tomatoes

1 large cauliflower, florets
halved or quartered

200ml boiling beef stock

200g sugar snap peas

Stews are perfect for a cold evening, and this one is packed with pleasing chunks of meat and plenty of fresh vegetables.

Spray a large non-stick frying pan with low calorie cooking spray and place over a high heat. Fry the steak for 2 minutes on each side and transfer to a plate.

Add the onions and garlic to the pan and stir-fry for 2-3 minutes. Add the oregano, tomatoes, cauliflower and stock and cook over a medium heat for 6-8 minutes. Add the sugar snap peas and cook for 4 minutes or until the stew is thickened and rich.

Cut the steak into chunks, return to the pan with any juices and simmer for a few minutes to heat through.

Serve the stew in warmed bowls with mashed potatoes.

chilli beef and vegetable stir-fry

serves 4

each serving is:

Free on Extra Easy

Free on Original

8½ **Syns** on Green

---

low calorie cooking spray

1 red chilli, deseeded and finely chopped

bunch of spring onions, finely sliced

3cm piece of root ginger, peeled and grated

4 garlic cloves, crushed

500g lean beef mince (5% fat or less)

400g mixed stir-fry vegetables

2 tbsp light soy sauce

2 tbsp dark soy sauce

This fabulous stir-fry tastes fantastic and it will be on the table in less time than it takes to order a takeaway.

Spray a non-stick wok or large frying pan with low calorie cooking spray and place over a high heat. Add the chilli, spring onions, ginger, garlic, beef and vegetables and stir-fry for 6-7 minutes or until the beef is cooked through and the vegetables are just tender.

Stir in both soy sauces and toss to mix well. Stir-fry for another 2 minutes or until piping hot, then serve hot in warmed bowls with your favourite noodles.

Instead of using beef, you could add 250g sliced mushrooms to the wok with the vegetables and 250g diced firm tofu (plain or naturally smoked) when you add the soy sauces.

steak au poivre with sautéed potatoes

serves 4

each serving is:

Free on Extra Easy

4 Syns on Original

14½ Syns on Green

---

2 x 300g cans peeled new potatoes in water, drained

low calorie cooking spray

1 tbsp dried rosemary

salt and freshly ground black pepper

4 thick lean fillet or sirloin steaks, all visible fat removed

2 tbsp mixed peppercorns, crushed

200ml boiling beef stock

1 garlic clove, crushed

4 tbsp fat free natural fromage frais

small handful of finely chopped fresh tarragon or 2 tsp dried tarragon

The classic French dish of steak au poivre (pepper steak) is so simple to cook and the irresistible sauce will have everyone asking for second helpings.

Preheat the oven to 220°C/Fan 200°C/Gas 7.

Put the potatoes on a non-stick baking tray. Spray with low calorie cooking spray, sprinkle over the dried rosemary and season well. Bake for 15 minutes or until lightly golden, then set aside and keep warm.

Meanwhile, season the steaks well with salt and the crushed peppercorns and lightly spray with low calorie cooking spray. Heat a large frying pan over a high heat, add the steaks in a single layer and cook until done to your liking (for a 2.5cm thick steak, fry for 1½ minutes each side for rare, 3 minutes each side for medium and 4 minutes each side for well done). Transfer the steaks to a warmed plate, cover and keep warm (if you can't fit all the steaks in your pan, cook them in two batches).

Add the stock and garlic to the frying pan and let it bubble away for 1-2 minutes over a high heat, then remove from the heat and stir in the fromage frais and tarragon.

Put the steaks on to warmed plates and spoon over the sauce. Serve with the potatoes and your favourite vegetables.

thai beef stew

serves 4

each serving is:

½ **Syn** on Extra Easy

½ **Syn** on Original

9 Syns on Green

---

low calorie cooking spray

4 shallots, finely chopped

2 garlic cloves, finely chopped

5cm piece of root ginger, peeled and finely chopped

500g lean beef mince (5% fat or less)

1 level tbsp Thai red curry paste

1 tbsp Thai fish sauce (nam pla)

1 tbsp dark soy sauce

4 dried kaffir lime leaves or zest of 1 lime

200ml boiling beef stock

400g frozen casserole vegetables, such as carrot and swede

100g fat free natural fromage frais

small handful of chopped fresh coriander

The distinctive flavours of South-east Asia steal the show in this mild and speedy Thai-influenced stew. Red curry paste, fish sauce and kaffir lime leaves tantalise the tastebuds, while the beef and vegetables satisfy the appetite.

Spray a large saucepan with low calorie cooking spray and place over a high heat. Add the shallots, garlic, ginger and beef and stir-fry for 2-3 minutes.

Stir in the Thai red curry paste, Thai fish sauce and soy sauce. Crumble in the kaffir lime leaves and add the stock and frozen vegetables. Cook over a medium heat for 7 minutes or until the vegetables are tender.

Remove the pan from the heat and stir in the fromage frais. Garnish with coriander and serve with boiled jasmine/Thai fragrant rice.

fast family
cottage pie

Not many meals are as filling and appealing as a cottage pie and you'll be tucking into this speedy version in just 30 minutes.

Spray a large frying pan with low calorie cooking spray and place over a high heat. Add the onion and beef and stir-fry for 1-2 minutes.

Stir in the kale, chopped tomatoes, passata, tomato purée, Worcestershire sauce and dried herbs. Bring to the boil, cover and cook over a high heat for 12-15 minutes, stirring often.

Meanwhile, cook the potatoes in a saucepan of lightly salted boiling water for 10 minutes or until just tender. Drain and roughly mash with the fromage frais, seasoning well.

Preheat the grill to high.

Spoon the beef mixture into an ovenproof dish and spread the mash over the top. Grill for a few minutes until lightly browned and serve with a mixed salad or vegetables of your choice.

If you're not the speediest of choppers you could buy prepared diced onion to save time.

serves 4

each serving is:

Free on Extra Easy

8½ **Syns** on Green

10½ **Syns** on Original

---

low calorie cooking spray

1 large onion, finely chopped

500g lean beef mince (5% fat or less)

200g prepared chopped kale

400g can chopped tomatoes

200g passata

6 tbsp tomato purée

a splash of Worcestershire sauce

1 tsp dried mixed herbs

1kg potatoes, peeled and roughly chopped

200g fat free natural fromage frais

salt and freshly ground black pepper

20

simple beef and mushroom stroganoff

serves 4

each serving is:

Free on Extra Easy

Free on Original

8 Syns on Green

---

low calorie cooking spray

2 onions, finely sliced

3 x 250g packs sliced white mushrooms

500g lean sirloin steak, all visible fat removed, cut into thin strips

400ml boiling beef stock

1 tbsp green peppercorns in brine, drained

½ tsp mustard powder mixed with 1 tsp water

salt and freshly ground black pepper

200g fat free natural fromage frais

small handful of finely chopped fresh chives, to garnish

Stroganoff is a traditional Russian dish made with sour cream – our super-speedy version has all the flavour and it's Free on Extra Easy and Original.

Spray a large non-stick frying pan with low calorie cooking spray and place over a medium heat. Add the onions and mushrooms and stir-fry for 5-6 minutes until softened. Remove with a slotted spoon and set aside on a plate.

Wipe the pan, respray with low calorie cooking spray and turn the heat to high. Add the steak and stir-fry for 2-3 minutes.

Add the stock, peppercorns and mustard and return the onions and mushrooms to the pan. Season well and leave to bubble for 2-3 minutes.

Remove from the heat, stir in the fromage frais and scatter over the chives.

Serve hot with boiled rice and your favourite vegetables.

speedy bolognese

The essential Italian pasta sauce is as popular as ever and it's always worth making double the amount and freezing half for a rainy day.

serves 4

each serving is:

Free on Extra Easy

Free on Original

8½ **Syns** on Green

Spray a large non-stick frying pan with low calorie cooking spray and place over a high heat. Add the mince and stir-fry for 2 minutes or until browned, then add the onion, carrot, celery and garlic and stir-fry for 1 minute.

Add the chopped tomatoes, tomato purée, passata and dried herbs, season well and cook over a medium heat for 12-15 minutes, stirring occasionally.

Stir the bolognese into your favourite pasta (we used pappardelle) and serve hot, with parsley scattered over.

Lean turkey mince or lean pork mince (both 5% fat or less) would work well instead of the beef.

low calorie cooking spray

500g lean beef mince (5% fat or less)

1 onion, roughly chopped

1 large carrot, peeled and diced

3 celery sticks, roughly chopped

4 garlic cloves, roughly chopped

400g can chopped tomatoes

4 tbsp tomato purée

500g passata

1 tsp dried mixed herbs

salt and freshly ground black pepper

small handful of finely chopped fresh parsley, to garnish

griddled beef
summer salad

serves 4

each serving is:

Free on Extra Easy

Free on Original

8 Syns on Green

1 red onion, halved
and thinly sliced

100g radishes, thinly sliced

1 red pepper, deseeded
and thinly sliced

1 yellow pepper, deseeded
and thinly sliced

small bag of rocket salad

salt and freshly ground black pepper

500g lean rump or sirloin steak,
all visible fat removed

4 tbsp fat free vinaigrette

juice of 1 lime

This super salad is packed with vibrant colours
and refreshing flavours – it's a wonderful way to
enjoy steak.

Put the onion, radishes and peppers into a wide salad bowl with the
rocket leaves.

Heat a griddle over a high heat. Season the steak and cook on the
griddle for 1½-4 minutes on each side, depending on how rare or well
done you like it. Transfer to a board and leave to rest for a few minutes.

Meanwhile, mix together the vinaigrette and lime juice.

Cut the steak into thin slices and add to the salad bowl. Drizzle
over the dressing, check the seasoning and toss to mix well. This
salad is great served with couscous.

*For a no-cook summer salmon salad, swap the steak
for 400g roughly flaked hot-smoked salmon and add
to the salad with the dressing.*

moroccan lamb

serves 4

each serving is:

Free on Extra Easy

½ **Syn** on Original

13 Syns on Green

---

low calorie cooking spray

4 large lean lamb leg steaks, all visible fat removed, cut into small chunks

1 onion, finely chopped

4 garlic cloves, crushed

1 tbsp ras el hanout spice mix

400g can chopped tomatoes

2 tbsp tomato purée

200g passata

500g frozen mixed vegetables

2 tsp dried mint

salt and freshly ground black pepper

1 romaine lettuce, leaves separated

Spice mixes are a great way to add depth of flavour to a dish when you don't have a lot of time to cook. The Moroccan blend ras el hanout is fantastic with lamb and gives this quick supper an exotic edge.

Spray a wide non-stick frying pan with low calorie cooking spray and place over a high heat. Add the lamb, onion and garlic and stir-fry for 2-3 minutes.

Stir in the ras el hanout, chopped tomatoes, tomato purée, passata, frozen vegetables and dried mint. Season, stir and cook over a medium heat for 10 minutes or until the vegetables are tender and the mixture is piping hot.

Roughly tear the lettuce leaves and divide between serving plates. Spoon over the lamb mixture and serve with plenty of couscous.

Ras el hanout is an aromatic spice blend that includes cardamom, nutmeg, anise, mace, cinnamon, ginger, peppers and turmeric. It's widely available in most supermarkets but you could use 1 heaped teaspoon each of ground cinnamon and cumin instead.

lamb, green bean and cherry tomato salad

ready in
20
minutes

This must-make-again salad is full of healthy and tasty ingredients competing for your fork's attention!

serves 4

each serving is:

Free on Extra Easy

8 Syns on Original

13 Syns on Green

750g baby new potatoes, halved

300g green beans

4 large lean lamb leg steaks, all visible fat removed

low calorie cooking spray

salt and freshly ground black pepper

200g yellow and red cherry tomatoes, halved

half a bunch of spring onions, thinly sliced

for the dressing

1 tsp dried mint

5 tbsp fat free vinaigrette

1 tbsp balsamic vinegar (optional)

Cook the potatoes in a saucepan of lightly salted boiling water for 10-12 minutes, adding the beans for the final 4 minutes of the cooking time.

At the same time, lightly spray the lamb steaks with low calorie cooking spray, season well and cook on a hot griddle for 4 minutes on each side or until cooked to your liking. Transfer to a warmed plate for a few minutes.

Put the cherry tomatoes and spring onions into a wide salad bowl. Drain the beans and potatoes and add to the cherry tomatoes. Slice the lamb and add to the salad.

Make the dressing by mixing together the dried mint, vinaigrette and balsamic vinegar, if using. Drizzle the dressing over the salad, toss to mix well and serve.

You could replace the potatoes with 500g penne pasta. Cook it according to the packet instructions, adding the green beans for the final 4 minutes of the cooking time.

harissa lamb skewers
with taboulleh

serves 4

each serving is:

Free on Extra Easy

11½ **Syns** on Original

14 **Syns** on Green

8 thin-cut lean lamb leg steaks, all visible fat removed, cut into bite-sized chunks

2 tbsp harissa spice mix or Moroccan spice blend

low calorie cooking spray

for the taboulleh

250g dried bulgar wheat

1 tsp ground cumin

1 tsp ground ginger

½ tsp ground cinnamon

4 tomatoes, roughly chopped

1 cucumber, roughly chopped

1 red onion, roughly chopped

small handful of roughly chopped fresh coriander and mint

juice of 2 lemons, plus wedges to serve

salt and freshly ground black pepper

Harissa brings the warming heat of North African cooking to these tempting skewers loaded with chunks of juicy lamb.

First make the taboulleh. Put the bulgar wheat, cumin, ginger and cinnamon in a dry non-stick frying pan over a medium heat and cook for 1-2 minutes. Transfer to a wide heatproof bowl and pour in enough boiling water to just cover the bulgar wheat. Cover with cling film and leave for 10 minutes or until the liquid has been absorbed.

Meanwhile, put the tomatoes, cucumber, red onion and herbs in a large bowl with the lemon juice. Season well and set aside.

Preheat the grill to medium-high.

Put the lamb into a bowl, sprinkle over the spice mix and season well. Thread the lamb on to eight metal skewers, spray with low calorie cooking spray and grill for 5 minutes on each side or until cooked to your liking.

Tip the bulgar wheat into the tomato mixture, stir in with a fork and check the seasoning.

Serve the harissa lamb with the taboulleh and lemon wedges to squeeze over.

pan-fried lamb with sautéed vegetables

serves 4

each serving is:

Free on Extra Easy

Free on Original

13 Syns on Green

---

low calorie cooking spray

1 large red onion, cut into small chunks

1 red pepper, deseeded and cut into small chunks

2 courgettes, cut into small chunks

1 fennel bulb, cut into small chunks

3 tomatoes, cut into small chunks

2 garlic cloves, crushed

2 tsp herbes de Provence

2 tsp dried mint

4 large lean lamb leg steaks, all visible fat removed

salt and freshly ground black pepper

small handful of roughly chopped fresh flatleaf parsley, to garnish

Tender lamb steaks are a real treat and this easy supper includes plenty of healthy Mediterranean vegetables that are as delicious as the meat.

Spray a large non-stick frying pan with low calorie cooking spray and place over a medium heat. Add the onion, pepper, courgettes, fennel, tomatoes, garlic and dried herbs and cook for 10-12 minutes or until softened and lightly browned, stirring often.

While the vegetables are cooking, spray the lamb with low calorie cooking spray and season well. Heat another large non-stick frying pan over a high heat, add the lamb and cook for 5 minutes on each side or until cooked to your liking. Remove the lamb from the pan, set aside to rest for a couple of minutes and cut into chunks.

Divide the vegetables between warmed plates and top with the lamb. Serve hot, scattered with parsley.

cajun meatballs
with broccoli rice

ready in
30
minutes

Meatballs are terrific crowd-pleasers and these fine examples are infused with the rich warmth of Cajun spices.

serves 4

each serving is:

Free on Extra Easy

8 Syns on Green

13½ Syns on Original

✱ (meatballs only)

500g lean pork mince (5% fat or less)

1 tbsp Cajun spice mix

1 egg, lightly beaten

low calorie cooking spray

300g dried long-grain rice

300g frozen mixed vegetables

200g frozen broccoli florets

Preheat the oven to 200°C/Fan 180°C/Gas 6.

Put the mince in a bowl with the Cajun spice mix and egg. Mix well, shape into 20 balls and space them out on a non-stick baking sheet. Spray lightly with low calorie cooking spray and bake for 20 minutes or until cooked through.

Meanwhile, cook the rice according to the packet instructions, adding the frozen vegetables for the last 8 minutes of the cooking time.

Drain the rice and vegetables and divide between warmed plates. Top with the meatballs and serve with salad leaves.

You can also cook these meatballs under a medium-hot grill for 15-20 minutes, turning them halfway through cooking.

herb-crusted pork with apple mash

serves 4

each serving is:

4 Syns on Extra Easy

14½ Syns on Original

18 Syns on Green

Pork and apples make perfect partners and this clever recipe features apples in the mash!

1 tbsp dried mixed herbs

80g wholemeal bread, crumbed

2 garlic cloves, crushed

8 thin-cut boneless lean pork loin steaks, all visible fat removed

low calorie cooking spray

salt and freshly ground black pepper

1kg potatoes, peeled and cut into chunks

2 red apples

Preheat the oven to 200°C/Fan180°C/Gas 6.

Mix together the dried herbs, breadcrumbs and garlic, then rub all over the pork and lightly spray with low calorie cooking spray. Season well and bake for 15-20 minutes or until cooked through.

Meanwhile, cook the potatoes in a pan of lightly salted boiling water for 12-15 minutes or until tender, then drain and return to the pan. Coarsely grate the apples into the potatoes, season well and roughly mash.

Serve the pork with the mash and your favourite vegetables.

You can use any combination of dried herbs: chives, mint and rosemary all work well.

curried pork with fruity couscous

serves 4

each serving is:

½ **Syn** on Extra Easy

14½ **Syns** on Green

23 **Syns** on Original

125g fat free natural yogurt

juice of 1 lime, plus wedges
to serve

1 tbsp mild or medium
curry powder

salt and freshly ground black pepper

8 thin-cut boneless lean pork loin
steaks, all visible fat removed

for the fruity couscous

500g dried couscous

200g prepared mango chunks,
diced

200g prepared pineapple
chunks, diced

2 bottled roasted red peppers
in brine, drained and roughly
chopped

half a bunch of spring onions,
thinly sliced

large handful of roughly chopped
fresh mint

juice of 1 orange

Spicy, aromatic pork goes brilliantly with a
filling couscous salad packed with delicious
fruit and veg.

Preheat the grill to medium-high.

Mix together the yogurt, lime juice, curry powder and some seasoning
and brush this mixture over both sides of the steaks. Arrange the
steaks on the grill rack in a single layer and grill for 12-15 minutes,
turning once, until golden and cooked through.

While the steaks are cooking, make the couscous salad. Put the
couscous in a wide, heatproof bowl and pour over enough boiling
water to just cover the grains. Cover with cling film and set aside for
10 minutes or until the liquid is absorbed.

Put the mango and pineapple in another bowl, along with the roasted
peppers, spring onions, mint and orange juice. When the couscous
is ready, fluff up the grains with a fork and add to the mango and
pineapple mix. Season and toss to mix well.

Serve the steaks with the couscous salad and lime wedges to
squeeze over.

*You can replace the pork with three large thickly
sliced courgettes: brush them with the curried yogurt
mixture and grill for 3 minutes on each side or
until tender.*

thai-style
pork patties

You'll love the Asian flavours in these tasty pork patties and the speedy stir-fried veg is the ideal accompaniment.

serves 4

each serving is:

Free on Extra Easy

Free on Original

8 Syns on Green

❄ (patties only)

Preheat the grill to medium-high.

Put the spring onions, chilli, coriander, lime zest and mint in a bowl with the pork and egg white. Season and combine well using your fingers. Divide the mixture into 20 portions and shape each one into a patty. Arrange on a non-stick baking sheet, spray with low calorie cooking spray and grill for 15 minutes or until cooked through, turning once.

While the patties are cooking, spray a large non-stick wok or frying pan with low calorie cooking spray and place over a high heat. Add the pak choi and mushrooms and stir-fry for 2-3 minutes.

Stir in the stock, bring to a boil and simmer for 1-2 minutes. Remove from the heat and stir in the Thai fish sauce.

Divide the patties between warmed plates and serve with the vegetables and boiled jasmine/Thai fragrant rice.

For even speedier Indian-style patties, replace the spring onion, chilli, coriander, lime zest and mint with 1½ tablespoons of mild curry powder.

half a bunch of spring onions, finely chopped

1 red chilli, deseeded and finely chopped

small handful of finely chopped fresh coriander

grated zest of 1 lime

2 tsp dried mint

500g lean pork mince (5% fat or less)

1 egg white

salt and freshly ground black pepper

low calorie cooking spray

300g pak choi, roughly chopped

250g pack sliced mushrooms

100ml boiling vegetable stock

1 tsp Thai fish sauce (nam pla)

everyday pork burgers
with red cabbage slaw

serves 4

each serving is:

6½ **Syns** on Extra Easy

6½ **Syns** on Original

14½ **Syns** on Green

 (burgers only)

1 onion, finely chopped

500g lean pork mince (5% fat or less)

a splash of Worcestershire sauce

2 tsp dried sage

2 garlic cloves, finely chopped

salt and freshly ground black pepper

low calorie cooking spray

salad leaves

2 tomatoes, sliced

4 x 60g wholemeal rolls

for the slaw

½ red cabbage, finely shredded

1 large carrot, coarsely grated

2 level tbsp extra-light mayonnaise

100g fat free natural fromage frais

juice of 1 lemon

We all look forward to burgers for tea and these prime pork patties served with a punchy slaw will keep everyone happy.

Preheat the grill to medium-high.

Put the onion and mince in a mixing bowl with the Worcestershire sauce, sage and garlic. Season well and divide the mixture into four portions, shaping each one into a burger.

Lightly spray the burgers with low calorie cooking spray, place on a grill rack and grill for 12-15 minutes or until cooked through and browned.

While the burgers are cooking, mix all the slaw ingredients in a large bowl. Season and toss to mix well.

Put the salad, tomatoes, burgers and a little slaw into the rolls and serve with the rest of the slaw on the side.

*Save 6 Syns per serving by leaving out the roll or using a **healthy extra b** choice.*

pork and mango noodles

serves 4

each serving is:

Free on Extra Easy

8 Syns on Green

17 Syns on Original

350g dried egg noodles

2 garlic cloves, grated

5cm piece of root ginger, peeled and grated

500g lean pork mince (5% fat or less)

1 red chilli, deseeded and finely chopped, plus slices to garnish

1 tbsp dark soy sauce

low calorie cooking spray

400g mixed stir-fry vegetables

2 tbsp light soy sauce

200g prepared mango chunks, roughly chopped

Succulent pork and sweet fresh mango go so well together, as this sensational stir-fry shows!

Cook the noodles according to the packet instructions then drain and set aside.

Meanwhile, put the garlic, ginger, pork, chilli and dark soy sauce into a bowl and stir to mix well.

Spray a non-stick wok or large frying pan with low calorie cooking spray and place over a high heat. Add the pork mixture and stir-fry for 3 minutes or until browned.

Add the mixed vegetables and stir-fry for 5 minutes or until just tender. Stir in the noodles and light soy sauce and remove from the heat.

Add the mango, toss to mix well and serve in warmed bowls, garnished with sliced chilli.

For a speedy chicken noodle stir-fry, replace the pork with 500g skinless chicken breast mini fillets and stir-fry for 3-4 minutes before adding the stir-fry vegetables.

pork escalopes with creamy mustard sauce

serves 4

each serving is:

Free on Extra Easy

10½ Syns on Original

21 Syns on Green

1kg baby new potatoes,
halved lengthways

200g prepared carrot batons

200g prepared sliced runner beans

salt and freshly ground black pepper

low calorie cooking spray

12 lean pork escalopes,
all visible fat removed

300ml boiling chicken stock

½ tsp mustard powder
mixed with 1 tsp water

1 tsp wholegrain mustard

100g fat free natural fromage frais

1 tbsp capers, drained

2 tsp dried tarragon

This simple, creamy sauce is sensational with pork – and, amazingly, it's Free on Extra Easy!

Cook the potatoes and carrots in a large saucepan of lightly salted water for 12-15 minutes, adding the runner beans for the last 4 minutes of the cooking time. Drain, season and keep warm.

Meanwhile, spray a wide non-stick frying pan with low calorie cooking spray and place over a high heat. In batches, cook the escalopes for 4 minutes on each side or until lightly browned. Remove each batch from the pan and keep warm.

Stir the stock into the pan with both mustards and boil rapidly for 3-4 minutes. Remove from the heat and stir in the fromage frais, capers and tarragon.

Divide the potatoes, beans and carrots between warmed plates, then top with the pork and spoon over the sauce to serve.

For a spicier flavour, replace the capers with a tablespoon of drained pink or green peppercorns in brine.

presto pork
and fennel pasta

Fennel brings a delicious hint of aniseed that is fantastic with pork. Combined with pasta, it's a hugely satisfying dish.

serves 4

each serving is:

Free on Extra Easy

8 Syns on Green

22 Syns on Original

Cook the pasta according to the packet instructions then drain and set aside.

Meanwhile, spray a large non-stick frying pan with low calorie cooking spray and place over a high heat. Add the onion, fennel, garlic, courgette and pork and stir-fry for 4-5 minutes.

Add the chopped tomatoes, basil, tomato purée and stock and bring to the boil. Cook for 7 minutes or until piping hot.

Season well, stir the pork mixture into the pasta and serve with a salad.

500g dried pasta shapes

low calorie cooking spray

1 large onion, finely chopped

1 large fennel bulb, finely chopped

3 garlic cloves, finely chopped

1 large courgette, grated

500g lean pork mince (5% fat or less)

400g can chopped tomatoes

2 tsp dried basil

2 tbsp tomato purée

200ml boiling chicken stock

salt and freshly ground black pepper

griddled gammon
with summer salsa

serves 4

each serving is:

Free on Extra Easy

Free on Original

15½ Syns on Green

4 unsmoked gammon steaks, all visible fat removed, halved

2 tbsp mixed peppercorns

low calorie cooking spray

for the salsa

1 small red onion, finely chopped

4 tomatoes, finely chopped

1 red chilli, deseeded and finely chopped

1 red pepper, deseeded and finely diced

1 yellow pepper, deseeded and finely diced

small handful of finely chopped fresh mint

small handful of finely chopped fresh coriander

juice of 2 limes

salt and freshly ground black pepper

Bring the fresh flavours of summer to your table whatever the time of year with this mouth-watering meal.

Using kitchen scissors, make little snips all the way around the edges of the gammon steaks (this stops them curling). Coarsely grind the peppercorns and spread them over the steaks.

Heat a large griddle over a high heat, spray the steaks with low calorie cooking spray and cook for 5 minutes on each side or until cooked through.

While the steaks are cooking, put all the salsa ingredients in a bowl, season and mix well.

Divide the gammon steaks between warmed plates, top with the summer salsa and serve with boiled rice.

cumin-spiced gammon
with mango salad

Gammon is always a treat and the warmth of the cumin complements the sweetness of the mango perfectly in this satisfying and speedy supper.

serves 4

each serving is:

Free on Extra Easy

Free on Original

15½ Syns on Green

Preheat the grill to medium-high.

Put the lime juice in a bowl with the cumin, ginger and cinnamon. Season and mix well. Place the gammon steaks on a grill rack and spoon the cumin mixture over them. Grill for 4 minutes on each side or until lightly golden.

While the gammon is cooking, make the salad. Put the mango and watercress in a wide salad bowl with the lime juice. Add the spring onions, red pepper and tomatoes, season and toss to mix well.

Serve the gammon steaks with the mango salad and boiled rice.

For a speedier salad, use a ready-prepared salad of your choice, dressed with lime juice and seasoning.

juice of 1 lime

2 tsp ground cumin

1 tsp ground ginger

1 tsp cinnamon

salt and freshly ground black pepper

4 large unsmoked gammon steaks, all visible fat removed, halved

for the mango salad

200g prepared mango chunks

small pack of baby leaf watercress

juice of 1 lime

4 spring onions, finely chopped

1 red pepper, finely chopped

2 tomatoes, finely chopped

ham and baked bean chunky soup

serves 4

each serving is:

Free on Extra Easy

4½ Syns on Original

6 Syns on Green

2 onions, roughly chopped

2 large carrots, roughly chopped

4 celery sticks, roughly chopped

450g lean ham, all visible fat removed, roughly chopped

300ml boiling vegetable stock

1 tsp smoked paprika

1 tsp dried mixed herbs

300g passata with onion and garlic

415g can baked beans

a splash of Worcestershire sauce

salt and freshly ground black pepper

small handful of chopped fresh flatleaf parsley

Baked beans get a makeover in this irresistible soup filled with healthy veg, tasty aromatic herbs and spices, and satisfying chunks of tender ham.

Place a large non-stick saucepan over a high heat. Add the onions, carrots, celery and ham and dry-fry for 2-3 minutes, stirring continuously.

Add the stock, paprika, dried herbs and passata and bring to the boil. Cover and cook over a medium heat for 10 minutes, then add the baked beans and cook for another 5 minutes.

Stir in the Worcestershire sauce, season, scatter over the parsley and serve.

bacon and
spinach fusilli

serves 4

each serving is:

Free on Extra Easy

6 Syns on Green

22 Syns on Original

500g dried fusilli or
other pasta shapes

2 x 200g packs baby
spinach leaves

low calorie cooking spray

10 back bacon rashers, all visible
fat removed, roughly chopped

100g lean ham, all visible fat
removed, diced or roughly chopped

2 garlic cloves, crushed

2 tsp dried sage

1 tsp dried red chilli flakes

salt and freshly ground black pepper

This tasty pasta dish is ultra-fast and so simple to make – and anything that includes bacon is good with us!

Cook the pasta according to the packet instructions then drain and set aside.

Meanwhile, place the spinach in a wide heatproof bowl, pour over just enough boiling water to cover and leave to wilt for 2-3 minutes.

Spray a large non-stick saucepan with low calorie cooking spray and place over a medium-high heat. Stir-fry the bacon for 4 minutes or until lightly golden.

Drain the spinach in a sieve and squeeze out any excess water. Roughly chop and add to the bacon, along with the ham, garlic, sage and chilli flakes, and heat through for 2 minutes.

Add the pasta to the spinach, bacon and ham and toss to mix well. Season and serve with salad.

all-day breakfast spaghetti

serves 4

each serving is:

Free on Extra Easy

6 Syns on Green

22 Syns on Original

500g dried spaghetti

12 back bacon rashers, all visible fat removed, roughly chopped

bunch of spring onions, roughly chopped

3 tomatoes, roughly chopped

4 eggs*

100g fat free natural fromage frais

salt and freshly ground black pepper

2 tsp dried parsley

Pregnant women, the elderly and babies are advised not to eat raw or partially cooked eggs.

This inventive pasta recipe has quite a bit in common with the much-loved fry-up and it's perfect for a lunch or dinner with the wow factor!

Cook the spaghetti according to the packet instructions then drain and set aside.

Heat a large non-stick frying pan over a high heat, add the bacon and most of the spring onions and stir-fry for 3-4 minutes. Add the tomatoes and stir-fry for a further 3 minutes or until softened.

Put the eggs in a bowl with the fromage frais, then season and beat or whisk well.

Add the spaghetti to the bacon mixture in the pan. Remove the pan from the heat and stir in the egg mixture. Toss thoroughly so that the eggs thicken in the residual heat, making a creamy sauce that coats the pasta.

Sprinkle over the parsley and remaining spring onions and serve with salad.

Freshly grated Parmesan is delicious in this spaghetti dish. Add it with the fromage frais for a cheesy twist (1 Syn per level tablespoon).

bacon, squash and sweet potato stew

Squash and sweet potato are seriously satisfying and they taste amazing in this luxurious stew.

serves 4

each serving is:

Free on Extra Easy

3½ **Syns** on Original

5 **Syns** on Green

Spray a large saucepan with low calorie cooking spray and place over a high heat. Add the bacon, onion, squash, sweet potato and garlic and stir-fry for 1-2 minutes, then add the chopped tomatoes, dried herbs, tomato purée and stock.

Bring to the boil, cover and cook over a medium heat for 8-10 minutes. Stir in the green beans and cook for a further 8 minutes or until piping hot.

Remove from the heat and ladle into warmed bowls to serve.

You can buy packs of prepared squash and sweet potato in some supermarkets. Any leftover stew can be made into a delicious soup by whizzing it in a blender with some more stock.

low calorie cooking spray

10 back bacon rashers, all visible fat removed, roughly chopped

1 onion, roughly chopped

600g prepared butternut squash and sweet potato chunks

2 garlic cloves, crushed

400g can chopped tomatoes

1 tsp dried rosemary

1 tsp dried parsley

4 tbsp tomato purée

300ml boiling vegetable stock

200g trimmed green beans

quick carbonara
with mushrooms

serves 4

each serving is:

Free on Extra Easy

6 Syns on Green

22 Syns on Original

500g dried penne or
other pasta shapes

12 back bacon rashers, all visible
fat removed, roughly chopped

2 garlic cloves, halved

low calorie cooking spray

1 large onion, finely chopped

250g pack sliced white mushrooms

3 eggs*

salt and freshly ground black pepper

small handful of roughly
chopped fresh chives

*Pregnant women, the elderly and
babies are advised not to eat raw
or partially cooked eggs.*

The classic Italian pasta dish has never tasted
so good – or been so quick to make!

Cook the penne according to the packet instructions then drain and
set aside.

Meanwhile, heat a large non-stick frying pan over a high heat, add
the bacon and garlic and stir-fry for 5 minutes or until the bacon is
crisp. Discard the garlic and set the bacon aside, keeping it warm.

Spray the pan with low calorie cooking spray. Add the onion and
cook for 5 minutes then add the mushrooms and cook for another
5 minutes or until softened.

Place the eggs in a bowl, season and whisk well.

Add the cooked pasta and bacon to the mushrooms, then remove
from the heat and stir in the eggs. Toss thoroughly so that the eggs
thicken in the residual heat, making a sauce that coats the pasta.

Scatter over the chives and serve with salad.

*Freshly grated Parmesan (1 Syn per level
tablespoon) is delicious in this dish. Whisk
it into the eggs before adding to the pasta.*

liver, bacon and leek

serves 4

each serving is:

Free on Extra Easy

Free on Original

11½ **Syns** on Green

---

low calorie cooking spray

8 back bacon rashers, all visible fat removed, thinly sliced

500g calf's or lamb's liver, cut into strips

3 trimmed medium leeks, thinly sliced

350ml boiling chicken or beef stock

2 tsp dried mixed herbs

1 tbsp pink peppercorns in brine, drained

4 tbsp fat free natural fromage frais (optional)

The classic British recipe has never looked as beautiful as this. Serve it with a comforting pile of mash for the full experience!

Spray a large non-stick frying pan with low calorie cooking spray and place over a high heat. Add the bacon and stir-fry for 3-4 minutes, then transfer to a plate using a slotted spoon. Add the liver to the pan and stir-fry for 2 minutes, then add to the bacon using a slotted spoon.

Add the leeks to the pan along with the stock, mixed herbs and peppercorns and bring to the boil. Cook for 3-4 minutes or until tender, then return the liver and bacon to the pan. Toss gently to mix well and cook for 2 minutes or until piping hot.

Stir in the fromage frais, if using, and serve with mashed potatoes and salad leaves.

Be careful to fry calf's liver very briefly as it becomes tough when overcooked.

poultry
pronto

Tasty, tender chicken is sensational in so many dishes, including speedy stir-fries, fast pasta suppers, enticing rice meals and warming, aromatic curries. Take your pick from our tempting recipe round-up, which also features time-saving feasts using lean turkey and delicious duck.

quick chicken pasta salad

serves 4

each serving is:

Free on Extra Easy

8 Syns on Green

22 Syns on Original

500g dried fusilli or
other pasta shapes

4 cooked skinless and boneless
chicken breasts, roughly shredded

half a bunch of spring onions,
finely sliced

3 bottled roasted red peppers in
brine, drained and roughly chopped

4 bottled gherkins in vinegar,
drained and roughly chopped

200g cherry tomatoes, halved

small bag of rocket leaves

4 tbsp fat free vinaigrette

salt and freshly ground black pepper

This speedy cold salad is bursting with fantastic fresh flavours and it's ideal for lunch or supper in warmer weather.

Cook the pasta according to the packet instructions, then drain and cool under cold running water.

Meanwhile, put the chicken into a wide salad bowl with the spring onions, peppers, gherkins, cherry tomatoes and rocket.

Add the cooked pasta and dressing to the bowl, season and toss to mix well.

For a seafood version of this simple dish, replace the chicken with 300g cooked and peeled prawns.

mild chicken
and vegetable curry

serves 4

each serving is:

Free on Extra Easy

4 Syns on Original

8 Syns on Green

low calorie cooking spray

4 skinless and boneless chicken breasts, cut into bite-sized pieces

2cm piece of root ginger, finely grated

2 garlic cloves, finely grated

2 tsp fennel seeds, crushed

1 tsp ground cinnamon

2 tbsp mild curry powder

700g passata with onion and garlic

400ml boiling chicken stock

2 x 300g cans new potatoes in water, drained

500g prepared diced carrot and swede

200g stringless beans, roughly chopped

salt and freshly ground black pepper

fat free natural yogurt, mild chilli powder and roughly chopped fresh mint, to serve

Chunks of succulent chicken, tender potatoes and a perfectly spiced tomato sauce will satisfy your hunger and dance on your tastebuds!

Spray a large non-stick frying pan with low calorie cooking spray and place over a high heat. Add the chicken and stir-fry for 3 minutes or until sealed. Add the ginger, garlic, fennel seeds, cinnamon and curry powder and stir-fry for 30 seconds.

Add the passata, stock and all the vegetables to the pan and bring to the boil. Season well, reduce the heat to a simmer and cook for 15 minutes until everything is cooked through.

Divide between bowls and drizzle with yogurt, garnish with mint and sprinkle with a pinch of mild chilli powder.

Serve hot with extra yogurt on the side, sprinkled with mint and chilli powder.

This curry is also delicious with turkey – use 400g turkey breast steaks instead of the chicken.

piri-piri chicken
with rainbow slaw

serves 4

each serving is:

1 Syn on Extra Easy

1 Syn on Original

9 Syns on Green

---

4 skinless and boneless chicken breasts, cut into long slices or chunks

low calorie cooking spray

for the marinade

finely grated zest and juice of 1 lemon, plus wedges to serve

2 garlic cloves, finely grated

2 tsp piri-piri seasoning

1 tbsp tomato purée

1 tsp dried coriander

1 tsp dried mint

salt and freshly ground black pepper

for the rainbow slaw

½ red cabbage, finely shredded

¼ green cabbage, finely shredded

2 large carrots, peeled and finely shredded

4 tbsp extra-light mayonnaise

100g fat free natural fromage frais

Portuguese cooking features plenty of piri-piri chillies, which are mostly grown under the hot African sun. This beautiful meal brings a little of that heat to your dinner table, although it's mild enough for everyone to enjoy.

Preheat the grill to medium-hot.

Make the marinade by putting the lemon zest and juice, garlic, piri-piri seasoning, tomato purée and dried herbs into a wide bowl. Season and mix well. Add the chicken to the bowl and toss to coat evenly.

Thread the chicken strips on to eight skewers and spray with low calorie cooking spray. Grill for 12-15 minutes or until lightly browned and cooked through, turning once.

Meanwhile, mix all the slaw ingredients in a bowl, season and toss to mix well.

Serve the chicken skewers with the rainbow slaw, lemon wedges and a big bowl of boiled long-grain rice.

Marinating makes the chicken even tastier so if you have time, it's worth leaving it in the marinade for 4 hours or overnight.

lemon and herb chicken

This simple, speedy marinade creates sensational chicken breasts that will be the highlight of any meal.

serves 4

each serving is:

Free on Extra Easy

Free on Original

8 Syns on Green

Preheat the oven to 200°C/Fan 180°C/Gas 6.

Make three or four slashes on each chicken breast and place in a shallow, non-stick roasting tray in a single layer.

Put the zest of one lemon into a bowl and add the juice of both lemons, the garlic and the dried herbs. Season well and spoon this mixture over the chicken, rubbing it into the slashes. Lightly spray with low calorie cooking spray and bake for 20-25 minutes or until cooked through.

Sprinkle the chicken with extra tarragon, if using. This is delicious served with boiled rice and your favourite vegetables.

4 skinless and boneless chicken breasts

2 lemons

2 garlic cloves, finely chopped

2 tsp dried tarragon, plus extra to garnish (optional)

2 tsp dried mixed herbs

salt and freshly ground black pepper

low calorie cooking spray

speedy chicken jambalaya

serves 4

each serving is:

Free on Extra Easy

8 Syns on Green

16 Syns on Original

---

low calorie cooking spray

1 onion, chopped

3 garlic cloves, crushed

4 skinless and boneless chicken breasts, cut into small chunks

350g dried long-grain rice

1 litre boiling chicken stock

1 tsp smoked paprika

2 tsp dried parsley

4 tbsp tomato purée

¼ tsp Tabasco sauce

1 bottled roasted red pepper in brine, drained

1 bay leaf

300g frozen mixed vegetables

salt and freshly ground black pepper

small handful of finely chopped fresh parsley, to garnish

One of the world's great rice dishes, jambalaya comes from America's Deep South and combines elements of Spanish and French cooking – it's fusion food that's also fantastically filling!

Spray a large, deep non-stick frying pan with low calorie cooking spray and place over a high heat. Add the onion, garlic and chicken and stir-fry for 2 3 minutes.

Add all the remaining ingredients to the pan and season well. Bring to the boil then cover the pan and simmer gently for 15-20 minutes or until the stock is almost absorbed and the rice is tender.

Serve scattered with parsley.

Jambalaya is also great with pork – use 500g lean pork mince (5% fat or less) instead of the chicken.

balsamic
chicken farfalle

Dark, mature balsamic vinegar adds an extremely more-ish sweet-sour note to this easy pasta supper.

serves 4

each serving is:

Free on Extra Easy

5½ **Syns** on Green

22 **Syns** on Original

Preheat the grill to medium-high.

Cook the pasta according to the packet instructions, adding the beans and pepper for the last 4 minutes of the cooking time. Drain and keep warm.

Meanwhile, season the chicken well, lightly spray with low calorie cooking spray and grill for 4 minutes on each side or until cooked through.

Spray a large non-stick frying pan with low calorie cooking spray and place over a medium heat. Add the spring onions and garlic and stir-fry for 1 minute before adding the balsamic vinegar and passata. Bring to the boil and cook for 3-4 minutes.

Add the pasta, beans, pepper and chicken to the passata. Toss to mix well, season and remove from the heat. Serve in warmed bowls, garnished with basil leaves.

For a creamy version of this recipe, add 4 tablespoons of fat free natural fromage frais after removing from the heat and stir to mix well.

500g dried farfalle or other pasta shapes

200g trimmed green beans, halved

1 orange pepper, deseeded and thinly sliced

salt and freshly ground black pepper

400g skinless chicken breast mini fillets, halved lengthways

low calorie cooking spray

half a bunch of spring onions, sliced

1 garlic clove, crushed

1 tbsp balsamic vinegar

400g passata

small handful of fresh basil leaves, to garnish

chicken and broccoli
noodle steamboat

serves 4

each serving is:

Free on Extra Easy

5½ Syns on Green

17 Syns on Original

350g dried thin egg noodles

400g skinless chicken breast
mini fillets

1 tsp Chinese five-spice powder

2 tbsp light soy sauce

2cm piece of root ginger,
peeled and grated

2 garlic cloves, crushed

1.2 litres boiling chicken stock

half a bunch of spring onions, sliced

1 lemon grass stalk, finely chopped

200g frozen broccoli florets

200g frozen sliced mixed peppers

There's so much to please the tastebuds in this wonderful Asian-style dish. Once you've finished the tender chicken, filling noodles and healthy broccoli and peppers, you can turn your attention to the delicious broth at the bottom of your bowl!

Cook the noodles according to the packet instructions. Drain, rinse under cold running water and set aside.

Meanwhile, place the chicken mini fillets in a bowl with the five-spice powder, soy sauce, ginger and garlic and stir to mix well.

Put the stock in a wide saucepan and bring to the boil. Add the spring onions, lemon grass and chicken mixture and cook over a high heat for 5-6 minutes.

Add the broccoli and peppers, bring back to the boil, then cover and reduce the heat to medium. Cook for a further 5-6 minutes, stirring in the noodles to heat through for the last couple of minutes.

Stir to mix well and ladle into wide, warmed bowls to serve.

Most supermarkets stock lemon grass now. To prepare it, discard the tough outer leaves and finely chop.

chicken with leek, mushroom and tarragon

serves 4

each serving is:

½ **Syn** on Extra Easy

½ **Syn** on Original

8½ **Syns** on Green

---

low calorie cooking spray

4 skinless and boneless chicken breasts, cut into chunks

1 large carrot, roughly chopped

4 trimmed leeks, sliced

2 garlic cloves, crushed

250g pack sliced white mushrooms

400ml boiling chicken stock

2 level tsp cornflour

large handful of roughly chopped fresh tarragon

salt and freshly ground black pepper

finely grated zest of 1 lemon

These mouth-watering ingredients are best known as partners in the classic pie. Our healthy version has all the flavour for a fraction of the Syns!

Spray a large non-stick frying pan with low calorie cooking spray and place over a high heat. Add the chicken, carrot, leeks, garlic and mushrooms and stir-fry for 3-4 minutes. Stir in the stock and bring to the boil.

Mix the cornflour with 2 tbsp cold water to make a paste and add to the pan with the tarragon. Cook over a medium heat for 15 minutes or until the chicken is cooked through and the vegetables are tender.

Season well and remove from the heat. Scatter over the lemon zest and serve with boiled long-grain rice.

zesty one-pan chicken

serves 4

each serving is:

Free on Extra Easy

4 Syns on Original

8 Syns on Green

4 skinless and boneless chicken breasts

low calorie cooking spray

350ml boiling chicken stock

400g can chopped tomatoes

1 garlic clove, crushed

finely grated zest and juice of 1 lemon

1 tsp Italian herb seasoning (or use a mix of oregano, basil and marjoram)

2 tbsp capers, drained

2 x 300g cans new potatoes in water, drained

12 silverskin onions in vinegar, drained

salt and freshly ground black pepper

small handful of fresh basil leaves, to garnish

Capers and silverskin onions add bite to this comforting chicken supper and, because it's all-in-one, you'll save on the washing-up!

Place the chicken breasts between two sheets of cling film and lightly flatten them with a rolling pin or mallet.

Spray a large, wide non-stick frying pan with low calorie cooking spray and place over a high heat. Add the chicken in a single layer and fry for 4 minutes to brown, turning once.

Add all the other ingredients, season well and cook over a medium heat for 10 minutes or until the chicken is cooked through.

Remove from the heat, garnish with basil leaves and serve with your favourite vegetables.

To save even more time, use four skinless turkey breast steaks instead of chicken breasts – there's no need to flatten them before cooking.

ready in
ready in
30
minutes

summer chicken
couscous

serves 4

each serving is:

½ **Syn** on Extra Easy

8½ **Syns** on Green

16 **Syns** on Original

Every mouthful of this spectacular salad includes lovely roasted vegetables, aromatic north African spices, filling couscous and plenty of fresh herbs – it's fantastic hot or cold.

1 courgette, cut into small pieces

1 red pepper, cut into small pieces

1 yellow pepper, cut into small pieces

low calorie cooking spray

salt and freshly ground black pepper

350g dried couscous

300ml boiling vegetable stock

4 cooked skinless and boneless chicken breasts, roughly shredded

large handful of finely chopped fresh coriander

large handful of finely chopped fresh mint

1 tsp ground cumin

¼ tsp ground cinnamon

juice of 1 orange

juice of 1 lemon

Preheat the oven to 200°C/Fan 180°C/Gas 6.

Put the courgette and peppers on to a large baking sheet, spray lightly with low calorie cooking spray and season well. Roast for 15 minutes until browned and softened, turning and spraying with low calorie cooking spray halfway through.

Meanwhile, put the couscous in a large bowl. Pour over the stock, cover and leave to stand for 10 minutes or until all the stock is absorbed.

Fluff up the couscous with a fork and stir in the chicken, roasted vegetables and fresh herbs.

Mix together the cumin, cinnamon, orange juice and lemon juice, pour over the couscous and stir through. Serve with crisp salad leaves.

For a low-cost veggie version of this salad, leave out the chicken and add a drained 400g can of chickpeas.

fast
five-spice chicken

If you're looking for a marvellous meal in a hurry, it's time to reach for the five-spice! This traditional Chinese blend gives chicken an aroma and flavour that no one can resist.

Mix the soy sauce, chilli sauce, wine vinegar, garlic and five-spice powder in a wide bowl. Add the chicken and toss to mix well.

Spray a large non-stick wok or frying pan with low calorie cooking spray, add the chicken mixture and stir-fry over a high heat for 5 minutes or until lightly browned.

Add the mixed vegetables and stir-fry for 3-4 minutes, then add the dark soy sauce and toss together for 1-2 minutes until piping hot.

Serve hot with boiled rice.

Turkey is also delicious in this dish – use 500g lean turkey mince (5% fat or less) instead of the chicken.

serves 4

each serving is:

½ **Syn** on Extra Easy

½ **Syn** on Original

8½ **Syns** on Green

---

4 tbsp light soy sauce

1 level tbsp sweet chilli sauce

2 tsp white wine vinegar

4 garlic cloves, crushed

1 tsp Chinese five-spice powder

4 skinless and boneless chicken breasts, thinly sliced

low calorie cooking spray

400g mixed stir-fry vegetables

2 tbsp dark soy sauce

golden chicken skewers with chunky salad

ready in
25
minutes

serves 4

each serving is:

Free on Extra Easy

Free on Original

8 Syns on Green

---

4 skinless and boneless chicken breasts, cut into chunks

2 red peppers, deseeded and cut into bite-sized pieces

low calorie cooking spray

small handful of roughly chopped fresh coriander, to garnish

for the marinade

150g fat free natural Greek yogurt, lightly whisked

2 tsp paprika

1 garlic clove, crushed

1 tsp ground ginger

2 tsp turmeric

2 tsp mild curry powder

2 tbsp tomato purée

juice of 1 lemon

salt and freshly ground black pepper

for the salad

1 cucumber, cut into small pieces

1 red onion, cut into small pieces

2 tomatoes, cut into small pieces

juice of 2 limes

Chunks of juicy chicken breast on skewers are irresistible and these are cooked in a gorgeous tikka-style marinade.

Preheat the grill to medium-hot.

Put the chicken and peppers into a wide, shallow, ceramic dish. Mix together all the marinade ingredients and some seasoning, pour it over the chicken and peppers and toss to coat well. Thread the chicken and pepper pieces alternately on to eight metal skewers. Place the skewers on a grill rack, spray lightly with low calorie cooking spray and grill for 5 minutes on each side or until cooked through.

While the chicken is cooking, put all the salad ingredients in a bowl, season and toss to mix well.

Serve the chicken skewers with the salad and boiled rice, garnished with coriander.

You can also cook the chicken skewers for 8-10 minutes in an oven preheated to 200°C/Fan 180°C/Gas 6.

speedy
chicken pilaf

Pilaf is known by many names from the Middle East to India but these dishes all have one thing in common: delicious and filling scented rice. Ours includes tasty chicken chunks too!

Cook the rice according to the packet instructions.

While the rice is cooking, spray a large frying pan with low calorie cooking spray and place over a high heat. Add the onion and chicken and stir-fry for 6-8 minutes or until the chicken is just cooked through.

Stir in the vegetables, curry powder and cinnamon and stir-fry for a further 4 minutes or until the vegetables are tender.

Drain the rice, add to the chicken and stir-fry for 1-2 minutes. Season, remove from the heat and serve with a dollop of fat free natural yogurt sprinkled with black pepper.

serves 4

each serving is:

Free on Extra Easy

5½ Syns on Green

16 Syns on Original

350g dried basmati rice

low calorie cooking spray

1 large onion, thinly sliced

400g skinless and boneless chicken thigh fillets, cut into small chunks

400g frozen mixed vegetables

1 tbsp korma curry powder or curry powder of your choice

½ tsp ground cinnamon

salt and freshly ground black pepper

fat free natural yogurt, to serve

garlic and thyme chicken with vegetable penne

serves 4

each serving is:

Free on Extra Easy

8 Syns on Green

22 Syns on Original

4 skinless and boneless chicken breasts

2 tsp dried thyme

2 garlic cloves, crushed

1 tsp dried red chilli flakes

zest and juice of 1 lemon

salt and freshly ground black pepper

500g dried penne pasta

400g runner beans, trimmed and diagonally sliced

100g prepared chopped kale

If you want a filling supper, you can't go wrong with chicken and pasta. In this easy dish the pasta is tossed with fresh vegetables for extra goodness.

Preheat the grill to medium-high.

Put the chicken breasts in a bowl with the thyme, garlic, chilli flakes, lemon zest and juice. Season and toss to coat well.

Arrange the chicken on a grill rack in a single layer and grill for 6 minutes on each side or until cooked through.

While the chicken is under the grill, cook the pasta according to the packet instructions, adding the beans and kale for the final 4 minutes. Drain, season and divide between warmed plates.

Slice the chicken thickly and serve with the vegetable penne.

griddled chicken with herb and vegetable rice

serves 4

each serving is:

Free on Extra Easy

8 Syns on Green

16 Syns on Original

350g dried basmati rice

4 skinless and boneless chicken breasts

1 tsp dried coriander

1 tsp dried red chilli flakes

1 tsp onion salt

2 garlic cloves, crushed

low calorie cooking spray

400g mixed stir-fry vegetables

225g can water chestnuts in water, drained and sliced

225g can sliced bamboo shoots in water, drained

small handful of roughly chopped fresh mint

small handful of fresh coriander leaves

salt and freshly ground black pepper

It's fun giving the chicken a good bash before it's cooked, and chargrilling on a hot griddle gives this easy supper an appealing smoky flavour.

Cook the rice according to the packet instructions then drain, refresh in cold water and set aside.

Meanwhile, put the chicken breasts between two sheets of cling film and lightly flatten with a rolling pin or mallet. Place the chicken in a bowl with the coriander, chilli flakes, onion salt and garlic and toss to coat evenly. Spray the chicken with low calorie cooking spray. Heat a large griddle until hot and cook the chicken for 6 minutes on each side or until cooked through. Slice thickly and keep warm.

Spray a large non-stick wok or frying pan with low calorie cooking spray and place over a high heat. Add the mixed vegetables, water chestnuts and bamboo shoots and stir-fry for 5 minutes or until piping hot.

Add the drained rice to the vegetables and stir-fry for 2-3 minutes until piping hot. Remove from the heat, stir in the fresh herbs, season and serve on warmed plates, topped with the griddled chicken.

mexican chilli chicken cups

serves 4

each serving is:

Free on Extra Easy

Free on Original

8 Syns on Green

You don't have to miss out on the spicy delights of Mexican food – these crisp lettuce cups are every bit as tasty and fully Food Optimised.

low calorie cooking spray

2 garlic cloves, finely chopped

1 red onion, halved and thinly sliced

1 large red pepper, deseeded and thinly sliced

1 red chilli, deseeded and finely chopped

1 tsp ground cumin

1 tsp paprika

4 tbsp canned chopped tomatoes

4 tbsp tomato purée

4 cooked skinless and boneless chicken breasts, diced

salt and freshly ground black pepper

small handful of chopped fresh flatleaf parsley, to garnish

8 large leaves from an iceberg lettuce

lime wedges, to serve

Heat a large non-stick frying pan and spray with low calorie cooking spray. Add the garlic, onion, red pepper, chilli, cumin, paprika, chopped tomatoes, tomato purée and chicken and stir-fry for 6 minutes or until the mixture is hot and the vegetables are just tender. Season well and scatter over the parsley.

Spoon the chicken mixture into the lettuce leaves, fold them over to enclose the filling and serve with lime wedges and boiled rice.

chicken and quinoa salad

This simple salad of chicken, apple and celery is refreshing and substantial, and any leftovers would make a great lunchbox filler.

Cook the quinoa according to the packet instructions then drain and set aside.

Meanwhile, put the chicken in a large salad bowl with the apples, celery, spinach and spring onions.

Mix all the dressing ingredients together in a bowl and pour over the salad.

Add the cooked quinoa and toss to mix well. Scatter over the egg and fresh herbs to serve.

Quinoa (pronounced keen-wah) is a firm-textured grain that has been eaten in South America for thousands of years. It's a great alternative to rice or couscous, and you'll find it stocked near them in most supermarkets.

serves 4

each serving is:

Free on Extra Easy

8 **Syns** on Green

8 **Syns** on Original

200g dried quinoa

4 cooked skinless and boneless chicken breasts, roughly shredded

4 red apples, cored and cut into bite-sized pieces

4 celery sticks, thinly sliced

small bag of baby spinach leaves

bunch of spring onions, trimmed and thinly sliced

2 hard-boiled eggs, peeled and finely chopped, to garnish

small handful of finely chopped fresh chives

small handful of finely chopped fresh mint

for the dressing

200g fat free natural fromage frais

3 tbsp fat free vinaigrette

2 tbsp roughly chopped bottled gherkins

salt and freshly ground black pepper

jerk chicken
with caribbean rice

serves 4

each serving is:

Free on Extra Easy

8 Syns on Green

16 Syns on Original

This quick Caribbean supper offers a mouth-watering marinade plus plenty of vegetables and juicy tropical fruit – an exotic feast for any night of the week.

350g dried long-grain rice

4 skinless and boneless chicken breasts

1 tsp dried thyme

1 tsp ground ginger

1 tbsp cider vinegar

1 garlic clove, crushed

1 tbsp light soy sauce

2 tsp jerk seasoning

salt and freshly ground black pepper

2 bottled roasted red peppers in brine, drained and chopped

1 large carrot, coarsely grated

1 red onion, finely chopped

200g prepared fresh mango chunks, diced

200g prepared fresh pineapple chunks, diced

juice and zest of 1 lime, plus wedges to serve

Cook the rice according to the packet instructions, then drain and set aside.

Meanwhile, preheat the grill to medium-high.

Make three to four slashes in each chicken breast and place in a bowl with the thyme, ginger, vinegar, garlic, soy sauce and 1 teaspoon of the jerk seasoning. Season and toss to mix well. Place the chicken breasts on the grill rack in a single layer and grill for 6 minutes on each side or until cooked through.

While the chicken is cooking, put the red peppers, carrot, onion, mango and pineapple in a bowl. Add the rice to the bowl along with the remaining jerk seasoning and lime juice. Season and toss to mix well.

Divide the rice between plates, thickly slice the chicken breasts and arrange on top of the rice. Scatter over the lime zest and serve with lime wedges to squeeze over.

You can swap the chicken for lean lamb leg steaks, grilled for 5 minutes on each side or until cooked to your liking.

vietnamese turkey noodle soup

serves 4

each serving is:

Free on Extra Easy

6½ Syns on Green

17 Syns on Original

500g lean turkey breast steaks, thinly sliced

2 litres boiling chicken stock

200g prepared carrot batons

5cm piece of root ginger, grated

2 garlic cloves, crushed

250g prepared shredded cabbage

350g dried pad thai or ribbon noodles

50g fresh bean sprouts, rinsed

half a bunch of spring onions, sliced

1 large red chilli, deseeded and shredded

1 tbsp Thai fish sauce (nam pla)

juice of 1 lime

small handful of roughly chopped fresh coriander

small handful of roughly chopped fresh mint

You'll find so much of what's great about Vietnamese food in this amazing dish: vibrant colours, an abundance of tastes and textures and a wealth of vegetables and fresh herbs.

Put the turkey in a large saucepan with the stock, carrot batons, ginger and garlic. Bring to the boil and stir in the cabbage.

Bring back to the boil and add the noodles, bean sprouts, spring onions and chilli. Cook for 5 minutes or until the noodles are tender.

Remove from the heat and stir in the Thai fish sauce, lime juice and herbs. Divide between large bowls and serve hot.

Chillies vary enormously in heat, from mild to very hot. It's a good idea to use gloves when handling and slicing chillies and also to wash knives and chopping boards as soon as you can after using them.

spiced orange turkey steaks

Orange adds a zesty note to the Asian flavours in this fabulous turkey marinade, and the amazing salad bursts with goodness.

serves 4

each serving is:

Free on Extra Easy

Free on Original

5½ Syns on Green

In a shallow dish, mix together the cumin seeds, chilli flakes, coriander, turmeric, soy sauce and orange juice. Add the turkey steaks and turn to coat well, then season and leave to marinate while you prepare the vegetables.

Put the spring onions, radishes and carrot in a bowl with the watercress, orange zest and vinaigrette. Season and toss to mix well.

Heat a large griddle or non-stick frying pan until smoking hot. Remove the turkey from the marinade, add to the pan and cook for 3 minutes on each side or until cooked through (when cut, the juices should run clear, not pink).

Serve the turkey steaks with the salad and a big bowl of couscous.

Instead of turkey steaks, you could use four lean lamb leg steaks, grilling them for 5 minutes on each side or until cooked to your liking.

2 tsp cumin seeds

1 tsp dried red chilli flakes

2 tsp ground coriander

½ tsp turmeric

2 tbsp dark soy sauce

finely grated zest and juice of ½ orange

4 skinless turkey breast steaks

salt and freshly ground black pepper

half a bunch of spring onions, shredded

12 radishes, thinly sliced

1 large carrot, peeled and shredded

small bag of baby leaf watercress

6 tbsp fat free vinaigrette

italian-style turkey steaks with crushed potatoes

ready in
20
minutes

Italian food is all about simple flavour combinations and this speedy recipe brings together syrupy balsamic vinegar, garlic and lemon to create a dish you'll want to make again and again.

Preheat the grill to medium-hot.

Boil the potatoes in lightly salted boiling water for 8 minutes then drain and return to the pan. Add the vinaigrette and lightly crush with a large fork or masher. Season well and keep warm.

Meanwhile, mix together the tomato purée, lemon juice, garlic and basil.

Arrange the turkey breasts in a wide heatproof dish in a single layer. Spoon the tomato mixture over the turkey to coat evenly. Lightly spray with low calorie cooking spray and grill for 5-6 minutes. Drizzle the balsamic vinegar over the turkey steaks then turn them over and grill for a further 5 minutes or until cooked through.

Serve the steaks with the crushed potatoes and your favourite vegetables.

Swap the turkey steaks with lean boneless pork loin steaks if you like, cooking them for 5 minutes on each side or until cooked through.

serves 4

each serving is:

Free on Extra Easy

4 Syns on Original

5½ Syns on Green

2 x 300g cans new potatoes in water, drained

4 tbsp fat free vinaigrette

salt and freshly ground black pepper

3 tbsp tomato purée

juice of 1 lemon

2 garlic cloves, crushed

1 tbsp dried basil

4 skinless turkey breast steaks

low calorie cooking spray

2 tbsp balsamic vinegar

ginger duck with stir-fried noodles

serves 4

each serving is:

Free on Extra Easy

14 Syns on Green

17 Syns on Original

4 boneless duck breasts, skinned

2 tbsp dark soy sauce

1 tbsp ground ginger

salt and freshly ground black pepper

350g dried medium egg noodles

low calorie cooking spray

400g mixed stir-fry vegetables

2 garlic cloves, crushed

225g can water chestnuts, drained and sliced

225g can bamboo shoots, drained

2 tbsp light soy sauce

Salty soy sauce and sweet ginger make the duck unforgettable in this sumptuous stir-fry, studded with crunchy water chestnuts and bamboo shoots.

Preheat the oven to 240°C/Fan 220°C/Gas 9.

Put the duck breasts in a shallow ovenproof dish to fit snugly in a single layer.

Mix together the dark soy sauce and ginger and pour over the duck, turning the breasts several times to coat. Season well and cook in the oven for 12-15 minutes.

Meanwhile, cook the noodles according to the packet instructions. Drain and set aside.

Spray a non-stick wok or large frying pan with low calorie cooking spray and place over a high heat. Add the mixed vegetables and garlic and stir-fry for 3-4 minutes, then stir in the water chestnuts, bamboo shoots, light soy sauce and the drained noodles and stir-fry for 2-3 minutes until piping hot. Divide between four warmed plates.

Remove the duck from the oven and slice thinly. Top the noodles with the duck and serve hot.

fish in a flash

Our superb selection of seafood recipes will help
you enjoy the fresh flavours of fish while keeping
your cooking firmly in the fast lane. Choose from
dishes including hot pots, tempting stews, filling
fillets and baked delights – we're sure everyone
will want to dive in!

speedy fish hot pot

serves 4

each serving is:

Free on Extra Easy

4 Syns on Original

8½ Syns on Green

low calorie cooking spray

4 trimmed leeks, sliced

400ml boiling fish stock

400g can chopped tomatoes

1 tsp smoked paprika

1 tsp fennel seeds

4 skinless cod fillets,
cut into bite-sized pieces

2 x 300g cans peeled new
potatoes, drained and halved

200g white cabbage or kale,
shredded

small handful of roughly
chopped fresh flatleaf parsley

Tuck into succulent chunks of fish in a tempting tomato sauce flavoured with fennel seeds and smoked paprika. It's satisfying enough to be comfort food in winter and refreshing enough to be a perfect summer dish too.

Spray a large saucepan with low calorie cooking spray and place over a high heat. Add the leeks and stir-fry for 1-2 minutes.

Add the stock, tomatoes, paprika, fennel seeds, fish, potatoes and cabbage. Bring to the boil, cover and reduce the heat to medium, then simmer gently for 10 minutes or until the fish is cooked through and flakes easily. Garnish with parsley and serve hot.

You can replace the potatoes with 250g small pasta shapes such as orzo or even broken-up vermicelli.

spicy fish nuggets
with zesty vegetables

serves 4

each serving is:

Free on Extra Easy

Free on Original

8½ **Syns** on Green

 (fish nuggets only)

small handful of fresh
flatleaf parsley

half a bunch of spring onions,
roughly chopped

300g skinless cod fillet

400g raw, peeled tiger prawns

2 garlic cloves, crushed

1 tsp dried chilli flakes

1 tsp ground ginger

salt and freshly ground
black pepper

low calorie cooking spray

for the
zesty vegetables

1 large courgette,
coarsely grated

2 large carrots, coarsely grated

2 tomatoes, finely chopped

finely grated zest and
juice of 1 lemon

1 tsp Worcestershire sauce

1 tsp Tabasco sauce

ready in **30** *minutes*

These tasty balls of fresh cod and prawn are infused with garlic, ginger and chilli and the side salad is truly stunning!

Put the parsley, spring onions, cod and prawns in a food processor with the garlic, chilli flakes and ginger. Season well and blitz until fairly smooth. Using wet hands, shape this mixture into 20 nuggets.

Preheat the grill to medium.

Spray the grill rack with low calorie cooking spray and arrange the nuggets in a single layer. Spray the nuggets with a little cooking spray and grill for 12-15 minutes, turning halfway, until cooked through and golden brown.

While the nuggets are grilling, mix all of the zesty vegetable ingredients in a wide bowl. Toss to mix well and serve with the spicy nuggets and a big bowl of couscous.

If you find grating courgettes and carrots too time-consuming, try using the grater attachment on your food processor.

quick smoked haddock kedgeree

The classic dish combining eggs, fish, basmati rice and aromatic spices was traditionally eaten for breakfast in colonial India but nowadays it makes a sensational meal at any time of day.

Add the eggs to a saucepan of boiling water and cook for 7-8 minutes then drain, cool in cold water for a minute or two, peel and coarsely chop.

While the eggs are cooking, place the rice in a wide, heavy-based non-stick saucepan and stir in the curry powder, garlic, ginger and cinnamon stick. Season well and pour in the stock.

Add the broccoli, carrot and fish and bring back to the boil. Cover tightly, reduce the heat to low and cook for 10-12 minutes. Remove from the heat and leave undisturbed for 5-6 minutes, still covered.

Flake the fish through the rice and divide between warmed plates. Scatter over the chopped eggs, chilli and coriander to serve.

To make this dish even speedier, halve or quarter the eggs rather than chopping them.

serves 4

each serving is:

Free on Extra Easy

7 Syns on Green

13½ Syns on Original

4 eggs

300g dried basmati rice

2 tsp mild curry powder

2 garlic cloves, crushed

1 tsp ground ginger

1 cinnamon stick

salt and freshly ground black pepper

750ml boiling fish or chicken stock

200g prepared broccoli florets

250g prepared grated carrot

4 skinless smoked haddock fillets

1 red chilli, deseeded and finely chopped, to garnish

small handful of roughly chopped fresh coriander, to garnish

herby
haddock scramble

serves 4

each serving is:

Free on Extra Easy

Free on Original

7 Syns on Green

---

4 skinless undyed
smoked haddock fillets

8 eggs

small handful of finely
chopped fresh chives

small handful of finely
chopped fresh dill

400g jar roasted mild Peppadew
peppers in brine, drained and
roughly chopped

freshly ground black pepper

low calorie cooking spray

Tender flakes of smoked fish are tossed through soft and tempting scrambled egg in this more-ish dish – it's a great choice for lunch or supper.

Place the haddock in a saucepan and pour over just enough water to cover. Bring to the boil and cook for 7 minutes or until the fish flakes when lifted with a knife tip. Drain and leave to cool a little before flaking the fish.

Meanwhile, whisk the eggs and add the herbs and peppers. Season with freshly ground black pepper but not salt as the haddock is salty.

Spray a large non-stick frying pan with low calorie cooking spray and place over a low heat. Add the egg mixture and cook gently, stirring often with a wooden spoon until the eggs have just started to set. Stir in the flaked fish, remove from the heat and serve hot with salad and boiled potatoes (we used Anya potatoes).

For an even quicker scramble, use smoked salmon trimmings instead of the haddock so you don't have to poach the fish. Add the salmon just before removing the pan from the heat.

basque-style hake
with mixed peppers

Sweet red onion and peppers make a wonderful match for delicate fillets of fresh hake in this memorable dish from the Basque region in northern Spain and southern France.

serves 4

each serving is:

Free on Extra Easy

Free on Original

8½ Syns on Green

Spray a deep non-stick frying pan with low calorie cooking spray and place over a high heat. Add the onion, garlic and peppers and stir-fry for 1-2 minutes. Stir in the oregano, paprika, tomatoes and vinegar and cook for 6-8 minutes.

Carefully place the hake fillets on top of the vegetables, pushing them in slightly. Turn the heat down to medium, cover and cook for 8 minutes or until the fish is cooked through.

Lift the fish and vegetables into wide bowls, scatter over the parsley and serve with boiled rice.

To make this a mixed seafood dish, replace the hake with 600g ready-cooked seafood mix and add to the pan for the last 4 minutes of the cooking time.

low calorie cooking spray

1 large red onion, halved and sliced

3 garlic cloves, crushed

400g frozen sliced mixed peppers

1 tsp dried oregano

1 tsp sweet smoked paprika

400g can chopped tomatoes

1 tbsp sherry vinegar

4 skinless hake fillets or skinless cod fillets

small handful of roughly chopped fresh flatleaf parsley

baked
rosemary monkfish

serves 4

each serving is:

Free on Extra Easy

Free on Original

5 Syns on Green

600g monkfish tail fillet,
cut into 2 pieces, or use
any thick white fish fillet

low calorie cooking spray

4 garlic cloves, thickly sliced

2 sprigs of fresh rosemary, leaves
picked and roughly chopped

finely grated zest and
juice of 1 lemon

4 large tomatoes, halved

salt and freshly ground black pepper

Fish-lovers will adore this simple recipe. The firm, almost meaty texture of monkfish is a joy to eat and its mild flavour works well with so many ingredients.

Preheat the oven to 200°C/Fan 180°C/Gas 6.

Cut two sheets of tin foil, large enough to enclose each piece of monkfish, lightly spray with low calorie cooking spray and top with the fish.

Make small cuts all over the fish and push in the garlic and rosemary. Scatter the zest and juice over the fish, divide the tomatoes between the foil sheets and season well. Fold up the foil to enclose the fish and tomatoes, seal the edges and bake on a baking tray for 15 minutes or until cooked through.

Cut each piece of fish into chunks and transfer to warmed plates along with the tomatoes. Serve with lightly crushed new potatoes and your favourite vegetables.

To make monkfish kebabs, cut 500g monkfish tail and four red peppers into bite-sized pieces and mix in a bowl with three finely chopped garlic cloves, 1 tablespoon of dried rosemary and the finely grated zest and juice of one lemon. Season well and thread the fish chunks and peppers alternately on to four metal skewers. Place on a non-stick baking tray and bake at 200°C/Fan 180°C/Gas 6 for 12-15 minutes or until cooked through.

grilled lemon sole
with golden couscous

serves 4

each serving is:

Free on Extra Easy

10 Syns on Green

16 Syns on Original

350g dried couscous

1 tsp turmeric

salt and freshly ground black pepper

200g trimmed green beans, halved

2 fennel bulbs, trimmed,
quartered and thinly sliced

2 tomatoes, roughly chopped

2 spring onions, sliced

2 tbsp capers, drained and rinsed

finely grated zest and
juice of 1 lemon

low calorie cooking spray

4 lemon sole fillets

It takes next to no time to assemble this special dish of grilled fish plus a fabulous couscous salad packed with fresh vegetables.

Place the couscous and turmeric in a wide, heatproof bowl and season well. Pour in boiling water to just cover the couscous. Cover the bowl and set aside for 10 minutes.

Blanch the green beans in a pan of lightly salted boiling water for 2-3 minutes.

Place the sliced fennel in a wide bowl with the tomatoes, spring onions, capers and lemon juice. Drain the beans and add to the bowl, season, toss to mix well and set aside.

Preheat the grill to high.

Lightly spray the grill pan with low calorie cooking spray and arrange the fish in one layer. Scatter over the grated lemon zest. Lightly spray with low calorie cooking spray, season, and grill for 7 minutes or until just cooked through.

Fluff up the golden couscous with a fork, stir in the fennel mixture and serve with the fish.

honey and
mustard salmon

serves 4

each serving is:

½ **Syn** on Extra Easy

½ **Syn** on Original

16½ **Syns** on Green

2 tbsp dark soy sauce

1 level tsp clear honey

1 level tsp wholegrain mustard

3cm piece of root ginger,
peeled and grated

finely grated zest and juice
of 1 lime, plus wedges to serve

4 skinless salmon fillets

200g cherry tomatoes

low calorie cooking spray

2 garlic cloves, crushed

1 tsp dried red chilli flakes

400g baby leaf spinach

This punchy marinade transforms simple salmon fillets into a sizzling Asian experience – serve with your favourite noodles to make the meal complete.

Preheat the grill to medium-high.

In a shallow dish, mix together the soy sauce, honey, mustard, ginger and lime juice. Add the salmon and toss to coat well.

Grill the salmon for 10-12 minutes, turning once, until firm and just cooked through. Scatter the tomatoes around the fish for the last 2-3 minutes of the cooking time.

Meanwhile, spray a large non-stick wok or frying pan with low calorie cooking spray. Add the lime zest, garlic and chilli flakes and place over a high heat. Add the spinach and stir-fry for 4-5 minutes or until just wilted.

Divide the spinach between warmed plates, top with the fish and tomatoes and serve with lime wedges and your favourite noodles.

Marinating deepens the flavour, so coat the fish in the honey and mustard mixture and chill overnight if time permits.

salmon curry in a hurry

If you need a curry fix and can't wait, this speedy meal is for you! We've used mild korma powder so everyone can enjoy it but if you want to turn up the heat, feel free to switch to something spicier!

serves 4

each serving is:

Free on Extra Easy

Free on Original

12 Syns on Green

low calorie cooking spray

1 large onion, finely chopped

2 garlic cloves, finely chopped

1 tsp ground ginger

1 tbsp korma curry powder

400g can chopped tomatoes

300ml boiling vegetable stock

salt and freshly ground black pepper

500g skinless salmon fillet, cut into chunks

500g frozen broccoli florets

small handful of finely chopped fresh coriander

Spray a large non-stick frying pan with low calorie cooking spray and place over a high heat. Add the onion and garlic and stir-fry for 1-2 minutes, then add the ginger and curry powder and stir-fry for 1 minute. Stir in the tomatoes and stock, bring to the boil and cook over a medium heat for 6-8 minutes.

Season the salmon pieces and add to the pan along with the broccoli. Cook for 5 minutes or until the fish is cooked through.

Remove from the heat, check the seasoning, scatter over the coriander and serve with boiled basmati rice.

spicy hot-smoked salmon noodles

serves 4

each serving is:

Free on Extra Easy

7 Syns on Green

17 Syns on Original

Noodle dishes are as filling as they are flavoursome, and this easy supper has tasty chunks of salmon and healthy vegetables in every mouthful.

350g dried egg noodles

low calorie cooking spray

1 onion, halved and thinly sliced

1 large carrot, peeled and finely diced

1 garlic clove, crushed

1 tsp ground ginger

1 tbsp mild or medium curry powder

400g frozen sliced mixed peppers

4 tbsp light soy sauce

salt and freshly ground black pepper

300g skinless hot-smoked salmon fillet, roughly flaked

small handful of chopped fresh coriander

limes wedges, to serve

Cook the noodles according to the packet instructions then drain and set aside.

Meanwhile, spray a non-stick wok or large frying pan with low calorie cooking spray and place over a high heat.

Stir-fry the onion and carrot for 3 minutes or until softened, then add the garlic, ginger, curry powder and peppers and stir-fry for 4 minutes or until just beginning to soften.

Add the drained noodles and about 2 tablespoons of water and toss everything together. Add the soy sauce, season and stir-fry for another minute.

Add the salmon and stir-fry for 2 minutes or until piping hot. Remove from the heat, scatter over the coriander and divide between shallow bowls or plates.

Serve hot with lime wedges to squeeze over.

For spicy ham noodles, replace the salmon with 300g roughly chopped cooked lean ham.

smoked salmon and prawn gratin

If you haven't cooked with smoked salmon before, this tasty dish with juicy prawns, healthy spinach and crispy breadcrumbs will show you just how good it can be!

Preheat the oven to 220°C/Fan 200°C/Gas 7.

Spray low calorie cooking spray into a wide ovenproof dish and spread the spinach over the base.

Mix the cornflour with a little of the stock to make a smooth paste. Put the mixture into a saucepan over a high heat, gradually stir in the rest of the stock and bring to the boil, whisking occasionally until slightly thickened. Stir in the spring onions and nutmeg and season to taste. Stir in the prawns and smoked salmon and spoon this mixture over the spinach to cover evenly.

Scatter over the breadcrumbs and bake for 15 minutes or until hot and bubbling.

Scatter over the parsley and serve hot with your favourite vegetables or salad.

You can save 1 Syn per serving by leaving out the breadcrumbs.

serves 4

each serving is:

1½ Syns on Extra Easy

1½ Syns on Original

9½ Syns on Green

low calorie cooking spray

300g baby spinach leaves

2 level tsp cornflour

400ml boiling vegetable stock

half a bunch of spring onions, sliced

a little grated nutmeg

salt and freshly ground black pepper

200g cooked and peeled prawns

2 x 120g packs smoked salmon trimmings, roughly chopped

40g wholemeal bread, crumbed

small handful of roughly chopped fresh flatleaf parsley

ready in

30
minutes

mediterranean baked trout

serves 4

each serving is:

Free on Extra Easy

Free on Original

10½ Syns on Green

---

2 red onions, roughly chopped

2 fennel bulbs, sliced and roughly chopped

10 unpeeled garlic cloves

4 skinless trout fillets

200g cherry tomatoes on the vine, cut into bunches

2 tbsp capers, drained and rinsed

low calorie cooking spray

2 tsp Italian herb seasoning (or use a mix of oregano, basil and marjoram)

salt and freshly ground black pepper

small handful of finely chopped fresh flatleaf parsley

The vivid pinks, reds and purples in this easy bake will take your breath away, and the healthy fresh veg and tasty trout will have the same effect on your hunger!

Preheat the oven to 220°C/Fan 200°C/Gas 7.

Scatter the onions and fennel over the base of a large, shallow ovenproof dish or non-stick, deep roasting tray. Add the garlic cloves, dotting them around the dish.

Arrange the trout on top of the vegetables and scatter over the cherry tomatoes and capers. Lightly spray with low calorie cooking spray and scatter over the Italian herbs.

Season well and bake for 15 minutes or until the fish is cooked through and the vegetables are just tender. Peel the garlic cloves.

Divide the fish and vegetables between plates, scatter over the parsley and serve with couscous.

15
minutes

smoked trout and artichoke omelette

serves 4

each serving is:

Free on Extra Easy

Free on Original

3½ **Syns** on Green

---

low calorie cooking spray

salt and freshly ground black pepper

8 eggs, lightly whisked

200g smoked trout fillets, skinned and flaked

1 bottled roasted red pepper in brine, roughly chopped

400g can artichokes, drained and quartered

small handful of roughly chopped fresh chives

The strong flavours of smoked trout and artichoke combine brilliantly in this healthy omelette, which will be on the table in a flash.

Preheat the grill to medium-high.

Spray a 25cm non-stick frying pan with low calorie cooking spray and place over a high heat. Season the eggs and pour them into the pan. Scatter over the trout flakes and cook over a high heat for 1-2 minutes or until the omelette has started to set at the base. Scatter over the red pepper and artichokes.

Transfer the pan to the grill and cook for 1-2 minutes or until set on the top and lightly browned.

Scatter over the chives, cut the omelette into quarters and serve with a crisp salad.

It's fun to experiment with different flavours in omelettes. Instead of using trout, artichokes and red pepper, you can use up leftovers from your fridge, such as cooked peas, ham and mushrooms.

ready in
30
minutes

quick tuna
pasta bake

serves 4

each serving is:

Free on Extra Easy

3 Syns on Green

22 Syns on Original

500g dried pasta shapes

200g quark

2 garlic cloves, crushed

1 tsp dried mixed herbs

3 eggs, lightly beaten

low calorie cooking spray

half a bunch of spring onions, sliced

300g frozen mixed vegetables

2 x 160g cans tuna chunks in brine, drained and flaked

salt and freshly ground black pepper

small handful of roughly chopped fresh dill

Having a few cans of tuna in your storecupboard is a great help when you want to get dinner on the table fast, and everyone will love the taste of this easy pasta bake.

Preheat the oven to 220°C/Fan 200°C/Gas 7.

Cook the pasta according to the packet instructions then drain and set aside.

Meanwhile, whisk together the quark, garlic, dried herbs and eggs until fairly smooth. Set aside.

Spray a large non-stick frying pan with low calorie cooking spray and place over a high heat. Add the spring onions and frozen vegetables, stir-fry for 3-4 minutes and transfer to a baking dish.

Stir the quark mixture, cooked pasta and tuna into the vegetables. Season, stir to mix well and bake for 15 minutes or until bubbling. Scatter over the dill and serve with salad or vegetables of your choice.

king prawn and potato stew

Tasty pink prawns are the stars in this Mediterranean-style speedy stew flavoured with aromatic fennel seeds and gently warming chilli.

serves 4

each serving is:

Free on Extra Easy

3 Syns on Original

7½ Syns on Green

Spray a large saucepan with low calorie cooking spray and place over a medium heat. Add the garlic, onion, fennel seeds and chilli flakes and stir-fry for 1-2 minutes.

Add the potatoes to the pan with the passata and bouquet garni and bring to the boil. Reduce the heat to medium and simmer gently for 10 minutes or until slightly reduced. Season well, add the prawns and sugar snap peas and cook for 5 minutes or until piping hot.

Remove the bouquet garni, scatter over the parsley and ladle into warmed bowls. Serve with salad or vegetables of your choice.

low calorie cooking spray

4 garlic cloves, finely chopped

1 large onion, roughly chopped

2 tsp fennel seeds

½ tsp dried red chilli flakes

2 x 300g cans peeled new potatoes in water, drained

500g passata with basil

1 bouquet garni

salt and freshly ground black pepper

600g cooked and peeled king prawns

200g sugar snap peas

small handful of finely chopped fresh flatleaf parsley

special
prawn fried rice

serves 4

each serving is:

Free on Extra Easy

4 Syns on Green

13½ Syns on Original

300g dried basmati rice

low calorie cooking spray

3cm piece of root ginger,
peeled and grated

3 garlic cloves, crushed

1 tsp Chinese five-spice powder

300g mixed stir-fry vegetables

300g cooked and
peeled tiger prawns

bunch of spring onions,
sliced diagonally

4 tbsp light soy sauce

The classic Chinese rice dish is an irresistible treat and we've used plump, juicy tiger prawns to take it to another level!

Cook the rice according to the packet instructions then drain, refresh under cold running water and set aside.

Meanwhile, spray a non-stick wok or large frying pan with low calorie cooking spray and place over a high heat. Add the ginger and garlic and stir-fry for 30 seconds before adding the five-spice powder and mixed vegetables. Stir-fry for 4-5 minutes, then add the rice, prawns, spring onions and soy sauce and stir-fry for another 4 minutes or until piping hot.

Divide between bowls and serve hot.

chilli
squid linguine

The combination of squid and chilli is popular around the world and this irresistible pasta version is much loved in Italy. Find out why in just 15 minutes!

Cook the linguine according to the packet instructions then drain, reserving 4 tablespoons of the cooking water.

Meanwhile, spray a large non-stick frying pan with low calorie cooking spray and place over a high heat. Add the garlic, chillies, squid and tomatoes and stir-fry for 4-5 minutes, then add the cooked linguine, lemon zest and juice, capers, mint and rocket. Add the reserved pasta water and cook for 2-3 minutes, tossing to mix well.

Season and serve hot.

serves 4

each serving is:

Free on Extra Easy

3 Syns on Green

22 Syns on Original

500g dried linguine pasta

low calorie cooking spray

2 garlic cloves, finely chopped

2 red chillies, deseeded and sliced lengthways

300g squid rings, thawed if frozen

350g red and yellow cherry tomatoes, halved or quartered

finely grated zest and juice of 1 lemon

2 tbsp capers, drained and rinsed

large handful of fresh mint, roughly chopped

small bag of rocket

salt and freshly ground black pepper

va va veg

Vegetables take centre stage in our fabulous collection of meat-free feasts. So if you feel the need for swede, are pining for peas or in the mood for mushrooms, these speedy and simple recipes are all guaranteed to leave you feeling full of beans!

chargrilled vegetable and basil pasta

serves 4

each serving is:

Free on Extra Easy

Free on Green

22 Syns on Original

500g dried pasta shapes

1 large courgette, cut into bite-sized pieces

1 large aubergine, cut into bite-sized pieces

1 red pepper, deseeded and cut into bite-sized pieces

1 yellow pepper, deseeded and cut into bite-sized pieces

1 large red onion, roughly chopped

2 garlic cloves, crushed

salt and freshly ground black pepper

low calorie cooking spray

200g passata with onion and garlic

small handful of shredded fresh basil

Stir this chunky sauce into your favourite pasta for an authentically Mediterranean and seriously satisfying feast.

Cook the pasta according to the packet instructions then drain and set aside.

Preheat the grill to medium-high.

Put the courgette, aubergine, peppers, onion and garlic into the grill pan, season well and mix together. Spray lightly with low calorie cooking spray and grill for 10 minutes or until softened and lightly charred, turning the vegetables from time to time. Pick out and set aside any vegetables that cook quicker than the rest.

Meanwhile, heat the passata for 1-2 minutes in a saucepan over a medium heat. Add the grilled vegetables and stir to coat well in the passata.

Stir the vegetables into the pasta, toss gently to mix and scatter over the basil to serve.

The chunky sauce would go just as well served with rice or couscous instead of pasta.

broad bean, feta
and orzo salad

serves 4

each serving is:

2½ **Syns** on Extra Easy

2½ **Syns** on Green

24 **Syns** on Original

250g dried orzo pasta

250g frozen broad beans

250g frozen peas

2 x 400g cans butter beans, drained

low calorie cooking spray

2 courgettes, coarsely grated

1 yellow pepper, deseeded
and roughly chopped

1 red pepper, deseeded
and roughly chopped

salt and freshly ground black pepper

small handful of chopped
fresh thyme leaves

100g reduced fat feta cheese,
crumbled

for the dressing

1 red chilli, deseeded and
finely chopped

5 tbsp fat free vinaigrette

juice of 1 lemon

1 garlic clove, crushed

Orzo is very filling and although it looks like rice, it's actually a delicious variety of pasta. It's perfect in this salad of beautiful vegetables and fresh feta cheese.

Cook the orzo according to the packet instructions, adding the broad beans and peas for the last 3 minutes. Drain and refresh under cold running water then tip into a large serving bowl with the butter beans.

Meanwhile, spray a large non-stick frying pan with low calorie cooking spray and place over a medium heat. Add the courgettes and peppers and stir-fry for 2-3 minutes or until softened. Stir into the bean mixture, season well and scatter over the thyme leaves.

Make the dressing by whisking the red chilli, vinaigrette, lemon juice and garlic together and seasoning well. Stir into the bean salad along with the feta, toss to mix well and serve.

If you can't find orzo at your supermarket, just use 250g dried long-grain rice instead.

zippy
chilli beans

serves 4

each serving is:

Free on Extra Easy

Free on Green

9 Syns on Original

low calorie cooking spray

1 large onion, roughly chopped

4 celery sticks, roughly chopped

2 large carrots, peeled
and roughly chopped

2 garlic cloves, crushed

1 tsp cayenne pepper or
chilli powder

400g can chopped tomatoes

4 tbsp tomato purée

420g can red kidney beans
in chilli sauce

420g can mixed beans
in mild chilli sauce

1 tsp dried oregano

salt and freshly ground black pepper

small handful of finely chopped
fresh parsley or coriander, to serve

Beans are full of goodness and this super-fast
combo makes them taste amazing too.

Spray a large non-stick frying pan with low calorie cooking spray
and place over a high heat. Add the onion, celery, carrots, garlic
and cayenne pepper and stir-fry for 2-3 minutes.

Add the chopped tomatoes, tomato purée, beans and oregano
and season well. Simmer, uncovered, for 10-12 minutes or until the
vegetables are tender.

Scatter over the herbs and serve hot with mashed potatoes and
your favourite vegetables.

*The delicious chilli bean mixture is also great served
with boiled rice or as a jacket potato filling.*

cheat's leek macaroni cheese

Our version of the ever-popular dish features tasty pasta mixed with cheese, mustard and quark – and there's no need to make a fiddly white sauce!

serves 4

each serving is:

2 Syns on Extra Easy

2 Syns on Green

23½ Syns on Original

500g dried macaroni

2 trimmed leeks, thinly sliced

200g quark

200ml boiling vegetable stock

1 tbsp onion granules

2 garlic cloves, crushed

1 tsp mustard powder

small handful of chopped fresh chives

50g reduced fat Cheddar cheese, grated

salt and freshly ground black pepper

Cook the macaroni according to the packet instructions, adding the leeks for the last 3 minutes of the cooking time. Drain and return to the pan.

Meanwhile, preheat the grill to medium-high.

Put the quark, stock, onion granules, garlic, mustard powder, chives and three-quarters of the cheese in a small pan and whisk to mix together. Heat gently until the mixture is fairly smooth and season well. Stir the sauce into the drained macaroni and leek and toss to mix well.

Spoon the macaroni mixture into four individual heatproof dishes arranged on a baking tray (or use a shallow casserole dish). Sprinkle over the remaining cheese, season and grill for 4 minutes or until golden and bubbling. Serve hot with salad or vegetables of your choice.

If you like a bit of extra spice, add 1 teaspoon of dried chilli flakes to the quark mixture.

middle eastern chickpea salad

This exotic salad is bursting with tasty vegetables, satisfying chickpeas and fresh herbs – and the zesty dressing makes every mouthful a treat.

Put the cucumber, tomatoes, spring onions, carrot, chickpeas, spinach and herbs in a wide salad bowl.

Mix together all the dressing ingredients and drizzle over the salad. Season, toss to mix well and serve.

Replace the chickpeas with two drained 410g cans of black-eyed beans if you fancy a change.

serves 4

each serving is:

Free on Extra Easy

Free on Green

7½ Syns on Original

1 cucumber, diced

4 large tomatoes, deseeded and roughly chopped

bunch of spring onions, thinly sliced

1 large carrot, peeled and coarsely grated

2 x 400g cans chickpeas, drained

small bag of baby spinach leaves

small handful of chopped fresh mint

small handful of chopped fresh coriander

salt and freshly ground black pepper

for the dressing

juice of 1 lemon

1 tsp ground cumin

¼ tsp ground cinnamon

2 garlic cloves, crushed

5 tbsp fat free vinaigrette

ready in
30
minutes

courgette and
aubergine dhal

serves 4

each serving is:

Free on Extra Easy

Free on Green

7½ Syns on Original

---

low calorie cooking spray

1 large onion, roughly chopped

2 garlic cloves, crushed

1 large aubergine, diced

1 tbsp mild curry powder

2 tsp black mustard seeds

1 tsp cumin seeds

200g dried red lentils

900ml boiling vegetable stock

1 courgette, sliced

2 large tomatoes, chopped

200g baby spinach leaves

salt and freshly ground black pepper

small handful of roughly
chopped fresh coriander

For millions of people in India and south Asia, dhal is the ultimate comfort food – a bit like mashed potatoes here in the UK. Ours is made with red lentils, which are cheap, easy to store and extremely filling.

Spray a large non-stick saucepan with low calorie cooking spray and place over a high heat.

Add the onion, garlic, aubergine, curry powder, mustard seeds and cumin seeds and stir-fry for 1-2 minutes.

Stir in the lentils and stock, bring to the boil and add the courgette and tomatoes. Turn the heat down to low and simmer gently for 15 minutes, stirring often.

Stir in the spinach and cook for a further 4 minutes or until the spinach has wilted.

Remove the pan from the heat, season and scatter over the coriander. Serve hot with boiled basmati rice.

easy, cheesy broccoli farfalle

serves 4

each serving is:

Free on Extra Easy

Free on Green

22 Syns on Original

500g dried farfalle pasta

400g prepared broccoli florets, halved lengthways

low calorie cooking spray

6 baby leeks, sliced

4 garlic cloves, crushed

1 red chilli, deseeded and finely chopped

1 tsp smoked paprika

200g low fat natural cottage cheese

2 tbsp capers, drained and rinsed

salt and freshly ground black pepper

Farfalle is one of the prettiest pasta varieties and it's great with the fantastic flavours in this easy supper.

Cook the pasta according to the packet instructions, adding the broccoli for the last 1-2 minutes of cooking. Drain, reserving about 4 tablespoons of the cooking water.

While the pasta is cooking, spray a large non-stick saucepan with low calorie cooking spray and place over a medium heat. Add the leeks, garlic, chilli and paprika and stir-fry for 4-5 minutes or until the leeks have softened.

Add the pasta and broccoli to the leeks along with the reserved cooking water, cottage cheese and capers. Toss to mix, season well and serve hot.

butter bean
ratatouille with eggs

serves 4

each serving is:

Free on Extra Easy

Free on Green

2½ Syns on Original

---

low calorie cooking spray

1 onion, roughly chopped

300g prepared chopped kale

3 courgettes, coarsely grated

3 garlic cloves, crushed

1 tsp smoked paprika

1 tsp ground cumin

¼ tsp ground cinnamon

salt and freshly ground black pepper

400g can chopped tomatoes

400g can butter beans, drained

8 eggs

This clever twist on the classic Spanish dish *huevos rancheros* is packed with deliciously healthy veg and topped with tasty eggs.

Spray low calorie cooking spray in a large, deep non-stick frying pan that can be used under the grill. Add the onion and cook over a low heat for 5 minutes, then stir in the kale, courgettes and garlic. Cover and cook over a medium heat for 5 minutes, stirring often.

Add the paprika, cumin and cinnamon and season well, then stir in the tomatoes and butter beans. Cover and cook gently for 5 minutes.

Meanwhile, preheat the grill to high.

Make eight small hollows in the vegetable mixture and crack an egg into each one. Cook over a high heat for 2 minutes, then slide the pan under the grill and cook for 2-3 minutes or until the eggs are just set. Serve hot with salad leaves.

For a speedier version, swap the courgettes for 300g frozen mixed vegetables and add with the kale.

ready in
30
minutes

lentil
ragù

serves 4

each serving is:

Free on Extra Easy

Free on Green

3 Syns on Original

low calorie cooking spray

1 onion, finely chopped

2 garlic cloves, crushed

2 large carrots, peeled and diced

4 celery sticks, finely chopped

400g can chopped tomatoes

1 tsp dried red chilli flakes

2 tsp Italian herb seasoning
(or use a mix of oregano,
basil and marjoram)

4 tbsp tomato purée

410g can green lentils, drained

200ml boiling vegetable stock

salt and freshly ground black pepper

small handful of finely chopped
fresh flatleaf parsley

A ragù is traditionally made with minced or chopped meat but lentils make a delicious (and much cheaper) alternative.

Spray a large non-stick frying pan with low calorie cooking spray and place over a medium heat. Add the onion, garlic, carrots and celery and stir-fry for 2-3 minutes. Add the tomatoes, chilli flakes, Italian herbs and tomato purée, increase the heat to high and cook for 5-6 minutes.

Add the lentils and stock and simmer, uncovered, for 10 minutes, so that all the flavours can combine. Season well, remove from the heat and scatter over the parsley.

Serve the lentil ragù with your favourite pasta (we used fettuccine), boiled rice or a jacket potato.

hot rice
and beans

This is a hugely popular combination across South America and the Caribbean. The rice and beans really satisfy your appetite and you can dress them up with whatever flavours you like best: we've used roasted red peppers, chilli and spinach!

Spray a large, heavy-based non-stick saucepan with low calorie cooking spray and place over a high heat. Add the onion, garlic and chilli and cook for 1-2 minutes, then add the red peppers and rice and stir-fry for 1-2 minutes. Pour in the stock, season and bring to the boil.

Stir in the herbs, cover tightly and simmer gently for 10 minutes. Stir in the beans and cook for a further 5 minutes or until the rice is tender and the beans are heated through.

Divide the spinach between wide bowls and spoon in the rice mixture. Scatter over the parsley and serve hot.

For a tasty change, replace the red peppers with two drained 400g cans of artichoke hearts in water.

serves 4

each serving is:

Free on Extra Easy

Free on Green

19½ Syns on Original

low calorie cooking spray

1 large onion, roughly chopped

2 garlic cloves, crushed

1-2 red chillies, deseeded and chopped

450g jar roasted red peppers, drained and chopped

350g dried basmati rice, rinsed

800ml boiling vegetable stock

salt and freshly ground black pepper

1 tsp dried thyme

1 bay leaf

410g can black-eyed beans, drained

small bag of baby spinach leaves

small handful of finely chopped fresh flatleaf parsley

feta and vegetable quinoa salad

ready in
20
minutes

This stunning salad is perfect for warmer weather, with freshness in every mouthful and creamy feta as the star of the show.

serves 4

each serving is:

4 Syns on Extra Easy

4 Syns on Green

12 Syns on Original

Put the stock into a saucepan over a high heat, add the quinoa and cook for 12-15 minutes. Drain, season well and set aside.

Meanwhile, blanch the green beans in a small pan of boiling water for 1-2 minutes. Drain, rinse under cold running water and drain again. Transfer to a wide serving dish with the cucumber, spring onions, tomatoes and herbs.

Mix together the dressing ingredients, drizzle over the vegetables and toss to mix well.

Mix the quinoa into the vegetables and scatter over the feta to serve.

Chicken is a good alternative to feta and makes this dish Free on Extra Easy. Use 400g cooked, shredded, skinless and boneless chicken breast instead.

600ml boiling vegetable stock

200g dried quinoa

salt and freshly ground black pepper

200g trimmed green beans, halved

1 large cucumber, roughly chopped

bunch of spring onions, sliced diagonally

200g cherry tomatoes, halved

small handful of chopped fresh mint

small handful of chopped fresh coriander

180g reduced fat feta cheese, crumbled

for the dressing

juice of 1 lemon

½ tsp ground cinnamon

1 tsp ground cumin

5 tbsp fat free vinaigrette

creamy mushroom pappardelle

serves 4

each serving is:

Free on Extra Easy

Free on Green

22 Syns on Original

500g dried pappardelle pasta

low calorie cooking spray

2 x 250g packs sliced mushrooms

1 large red pepper, deseeded and diced

400g can chopped tomatoes

100g quark, whisked

1 tbsp Italian herb seasoning (or use 1 tsp each of oregano, basil and marjoram)

150ml boiling vegetable stock

1 tbsp tomato purée

salt and freshly ground black pepper

small handful of chopped fresh tarragon

This simple creamy sauce makes mushrooms sensationally savoury. We've served them with chunky pappardelle pasta but spaghetti or fettuccine would be just as tasty.

Cook the pasta according to the packet instructions then drain and tip into a wide serving bowl.

Meanwhile, spray a large non-stick frying pan with low calorie cooking spray and fry the mushrooms over a high heat for 5 minutes.

Add the red pepper and fry for 2 minutes, then add the chopped tomatoes, quark, dried herbs, stock and tomato purée. Bring to the boil, stirring constantly, then turn down the heat and simmer for 6-8 minutes.

Stir the mushroom sauce into the pasta, season and toss to mix well. Scatter over the tarragon and serve in warmed bowls with a salad or vegetables of your choice.

mixed pepper
piperade

serves 4

each serving is:

Free on Extra Easy

Free on Green

Free on Original

---

low calorie cooking spray

1 large red onion, sliced

2 garlic cloves, crushed

2 large yellow peppers, deseeded and sliced

2 tsp herbes de Provence

3 bottled roasted red peppers in brine, drained and sliced

salt and freshly ground black pepper

4 eggs, lightly beaten*

small handful of finely chopped fresh flatleaf parsley, to garnish

Pregnant women, the elderly and babies are advised not to eat raw or partially cooked eggs.

If you like peppers you'll love this classic Basque dish, which mixes fresh and bottled peppers with soft, scrambled egg.

Spray a large non-stick frying pan with low calorie cooking spray and place over a medium-high heat. Add the onion, garlic and yellow peppers and cook for 4 minutes or until the onions are beginning to soften. Stir in the dried herbs and roasted peppers and cook for 3-4 minutes. Season well.

Pour in the eggs and cook for 2-3 minutes, stirring to softly scramble them.

Scatter over the parsley and serve with boiled rice and salad leaves.

You can speed things up by replacing the yellow peppers with 200g frozen sliced mixed peppers.

pea and
cauliflower pilau

The ultimate speedy veg curry, this will be ready faster than you can collect a takeout!

serves 4

each serving is:

Free on Extra Easy

Free on Green

16 Syns on Original

Spray a wide, heavy-based non-stick saucepan with low calorie cooking spray and place over a high heat. Add the onion, garlic, cauliflower and carrots and stir-fry for 1-2 minutes. Add the curry powder, chilli flakes and rice and stir-fry for 1-2 minutes.

Stir in the tomatoes, stock and peas and bring to the boil. Cover tightly, reduce the heat to low and cook for 12-15 minutes or until the rice is tender and the liquid has been absorbed.

Scatter over the herbs and serve in wide bowls with a side dish of yogurt sprinkled with chilli flakes.

low calorie cooking spray

1 large onion, finely chopped

1 garlic clove, crushed

1 large cauliflower, broken into florets

2 large carrots, peeled and roughly chopped

1 tbsp mild curry powder

1 tsp dried red chilli flakes, plus extra to serve

300g dried basmati rice

400g can chopped tomatoes

500ml boiling vegetable stock

250g frozen peas

small handful of chopped fresh mint

small handful of chopped fresh coriander

fat free natural yogurt, to serve

ready in

20

minutes

courgette
ribbon pasta

serves 4

each serving is:

Free on Extra Easy

Free on Green

22 Syns on Original

500g dried pasta shapes

low calorie cooking spray

4 courgettes, sliced into ribbons
with a vegetable peeler

salt and freshly ground black pepper

2 garlic cloves, crushed

finely grated zest of ½ lemon

4 tbsp fat free natural fromage frais

large handful of shredded fresh mint

Slicing courgettes with a peeler is a doddle and
turns this simple pasta supper into something
spectacular!

Cook the pasta according to the packet instructions.

Meanwhile, spray a large frying pan with low calorie cooking spray
and place over a medium-high heat. Add the courgettes and a good
pinch of salt and sauté for 5 minutes. Add the garlic and lemon zest
and stir-fry for 1 minute.

Remove the frying pan from the heat and stir in a couple of
tablespoons of the pasta cooking water and the fromage frais.
Season with black pepper.

Drain the pasta and stir in the courgette mixture and mint. Toss to
mix well and serve hot.

*Freshly grated Parmesan or a vegetarian alternative
(1 Syn per level tablespoon) is fantastic in this dish —
scatter it over the top just before serving.*

spinach and red pepper tortilla

The Spanish tortilla is like a frittata with sliced potato added, which makes it fantastically filling. The other ingredients are up to you – we've used leafy green spinach and tasty bottled peppers.

serves 4

each serving is:

Free on Extra Easy

Free on Green

1½ **Syns** on Original

200g baby spinach leaves

low calorie cooking spray

1 onion, finely chopped

1 tsp cumin seeds

1 tsp dried red chilli flakes

2 garlic cloves, crushed

2 bottled roasted red peppers in brine, drained and roughly chopped

300g can new potatoes in water, drained and sliced

5 eggs

1 tbsp dried tarragon

1 tbsp dried parsley

salt and freshly ground black pepper

Put the spinach in a wide colander and pour over boiling water to wilt the leaves. Drain, squeeze out any excess moisture with the back of a spoon, roughly chop and set aside.

Spray a 20-23cm non-stick frying pan with low calorie cooking spray and place over a high heat. Add the onion and stir-fry for 1-2 minutes, then add the cumin seeds, chilli flakes, garlic, red peppers, potatoes and spinach and stir-fry for a further 1-2 minutes.

Beat the eggs with the dried herbs and season well. Pour this mixture over the vegetables, tipping the pan so that the egg spreads evenly. Cook gently for 10 minutes.

Meanwhile, preheat the grill to high.

Put the frying pan under the grill and cook for 1-2 minutes or until the top is set and golden.

Cut the tortilla into wedges and serve with your favourite salad or vegetables.

speedy
asparagus penne

serves 4

each serving is:

Free on Extra Easy

Free on Green

24 Syns on Original

500g dried penne pasta

low calorie cooking spray

3 garlic cloves, crushed

350g asparagus, trimmed
and halved

salt and freshly ground black pepper

400g cherry tomatoes

200g frozen peas

200ml boiling vegetable stock

small handful of chopped
fresh basil leaves

This quick pasta dish is full of delightful fresh flavours – it's the perfect choice when asparagus is in season or whenever you want a taste of spring on your plate.

Cook the pasta according to the packet instructions, then drain, reserving about 4 tablespoons of the pasta cooking water.

Meanwhile, spray a large non-stick frying pan with low calorie cooking spray and place over a medium heat. Add the garlic and stir-fry for 1 minute, then add the asparagus, season, and stir-fry for 3 minutes until slightly soft. Add the cherry tomatoes and peas and cook for a further 2 minutes.

Pour the stock into the pan and bring the mixture to a simmer. Cook until the tomatoes start to burst and the stock is reduced by half – this will take about 5 minutes.

Transfer the asparagus mixture to a large serving bowl. Add the pasta and toss well, adding as much of the reserved cooking water as you need to loosen the pasta. Stir in the basil and serve hot.

cheesy
bean grill

serves 4

each serving is:

1 Syn on Extra Easy

1 Syn on Green

10½ Syns on Original

low calorie cooking spray

1 large onion, finely chopped

2 garlic cloves, finely chopped

600g frozen mixed vegetables

250ml boiling vegetable stock

2 x 415g cans baked beans
in tomato sauce

4 tbsp tomato purée

1 tsp dried thyme

1 tsp smoked paprika

30g reduced fat Cheddar
cheese, grated

small handful of roughly chopped
fresh flatleaf parsley, to garnish

*Humble baked beans get the VIP treatment
in this extremely more-ish grilled dinner –
and a little bit of Cheddar on top goes a
very long way!*

Spray a wide non-stick saucepan with low calorie cooking spray
and place over a medium-high heat. Add the onion, garlic and
mixed vegetables and stir-fry for 5 minutes or until softened and
lightly browned.

Add the stock, beans, tomato purée, thyme and paprika. Bring to
the boil, reduce the heat to medium and cook for 12-15 minutes.

Meanwhile, preheat the grill to hot.

Transfer the bean mixture to a heatproof dish, scatter over the
cheese and grill for 5 minutes or until lightly browned. Garnish
with parsley and serve hot with mashed potatoes and your
choice of vegetables.

*This meal also looks fantastic served in four
individual heatproof dishes.*

ready in

30
minutes

roasted
stuffed peppers

serves 4

each serving is:

Free on Extra Easy

Free on Green

11½ Syns on Original

---

salt and freshly ground black pepper

2 large red peppers, halved lengthways and deseeded

2 large yellow peppers, halved lengthways and deseeded

low calorie cooking spray

bunch of spring onions, sliced

1 garlic clove, crushed

1 red chilli, deseeded and finely chopped

1 tsp dried mixed herbs

2 tbsp tomato purée

200g dried long-grain rice

400ml boiling vegetable stock

400g can butter beans, drained

small handful of roughly chopped fresh flatleaf parsley

As well as being easy on the eye, these pretty peppers are packed with exciting flavours plus plenty of filling rice and beans.

Preheat the oven to 220°C/Fan 200°C/Gas 7.

Season inside each pepper half, place them cut side down on a non-stick baking tray and roast for 12-15 minutes or until just softened.

While the peppers are roasting, spray a large non-stick saucepan with low calorie cooking spray and place over a medium heat. Add the spring onions, garlic and chilli and stir-fry for 30 seconds. Stir in the dried herbs, tomato purée and rice.

Pour in the stock, stir and bring the mixture to the boil. Cook for 10-12 minutes or until the rice is just tender and most of the stock has been absorbed. Stir in the butter beans and season to taste.

Remove the pepper halves from the oven, leaving the oven on. Spoon the rice mixture into the peppers until they are completely filled with a nicely rounded top.

Return the filled peppers to the oven and bake for 5 minutes or until the tops are lightly browned. Scatter over the parsley and serve hot with salad leaves.

Other canned beans such as cannellini or pinto would work just as well as butter beans.

spicy squash and cottage cheese pasta

Squash and chilli is always an exciting partnership, and cottage cheese adds a touch of luxury to this satisfying pasta dish.

serves 4

each serving is:

Free on Extra Easy

Free on Green

22 Syns on Original

500g dried pasta shapes

600g prepared butternut squash

low calorie cooking spray

1 tsp dried red chilli flakes

2 tsp cumin seeds

200g bag baby spinach leaves

200g low fat natural cottage cheese

salt and freshly ground black pepper

Cook the pasta and squash in a large pan of lightly salted boiling water for 12 minutes or until the squash is soft and the pasta is al dente. Drain, reserving 4 tablespoons of the cooking water.

Spray a large, wide non-stick frying pan with low calorie cooking spray and place over a low heat. Stir in the chilli flakes and cumin seeds and cook for 1 minute, then add the pasta, squash, spinach and reserved cooking liquid. Stir to combine and cook gently for 3 minutes or until the spinach has wilted.

Remove the pan from the heat and stir in the cottage cheese. Season to taste, toss to mix well and serve with salad or vegetables of your choice.

sweet and spicy chickpea rice

serves 4

each serving is:

Free on Extra Easy

Free on Green

17 Syns on Original

300g dried long-grain rice

400g can chickpeas, drained

finely grated zest and juice of 1 lime

¼ tsp sweetener

1 tsp cumin seeds

1 tbsp medium curry powder

2 tsp dried coriander

1 tsp dried mint

low calorie cooking spray

2 large red onions, sliced

2 large red peppers, deseeded and sliced

400g baby plum tomatoes, halved

Warming, aromatic spices make this quick curried rice dish one that you'll want to make again and again.

Cook the rice according to the packet instructions then drain and keep warm.

Meanwhile, put the chickpeas in a bowl with the lime zest and juice, sweetener, cumin seeds, curry powder, coriander and mint. Stir well to coat the chickpeas.

Spray a large non-stick frying pan with low calorie cooking spray and place over a high heat. Add the onions and stir-fry for 4 minutes or until just beginning to colour. Reduce the heat to medium, add the peppers and cook for a further 3-4 minutes until the vegetables are just tender, stirring occasionally.

Stir in the tomatoes, chickpea mixture and cooked rice. Stir-fry for 2 minutes or until everything is piping hot, then serve.

This would also be fantastic with couscous. Cook the couscous according to the packet instructions and stir in instead of the cooked rice.

quick veggie cassoulet

serves 4

each serving is:

Free on Extra Easy

Free on Green

7 Syns on Original

low calorie cooking spray

1 onion, roughly chopped

3 garlic cloves, crushed

1 large carrot, peeled
and roughly chopped

1 fennel bulb, roughly chopped

2 x 400g cans chopped tomatoes

4 tbsp tomato purée

2 tsp dried thyme

410g can cannellini beans, drained

400g can pinto beans, drained

salt and freshly ground black pepper

300g pack Quorn
Chicken-Style Pieces

small handful of roughly chopped
fresh parsley, to garnish

The classic French casserole is normally made with a variety of high-Syn meats and takes hours in the oven – but our light version is Free and it's on the table in just 30 minutes!

Spray a large non-stick saucepan with low calorie cooking spray and place over a high heat. Add the onion, garlic, carrot and fennel and stir-fry for 2-3 minutes.

Add the tomatoes, tomato purée, thyme and beans, season well and bring to the boil. Reduce the heat to medium and cook, uncovered, for 15 minutes.

Stir in the Quorn pieces and cook for 1-2 minutes to heat through. Scatter over the parsley and serve hot with a big bowl of couscous.

For extra spice, add a generous splash of Tabasco sauce just before serving.

desserts at the double

After getting dinner on the table so speedily, use some of the time saved to create a deliciously sweet finale! Choose from irresistible desserts including fantastic fig tartlets, ravishing raspberry meringues and a five-minute tutti frutti sorbet.

lemon, passion fruit
and honey zabaglione

serves 4

each serving is:

1 Syn on Extra Easy

1 Syn on Green

1 Syn on Original

6 passion fruits

2 tsp sweetener

1 level tbsp clear honey

¼ tsp ground cinnamon

4 egg yolks*

finely grated zest and
juice of ½ lemon

175g pot Muller Light Vanilla yogurt

*Pregnant women, the elderly and
babies are advised not to eat raw
or partially cooked eggs.*

*Zabaglione is a delicious Italian dessert and a
distant cousin of custard. It takes a little while
to whisk the eggs but the wow factor more than
repays the effort!*

Half-fill a saucepan with boiling water and bring to a simmer.

Put the pulp and seeds of the passion fruit into a heatproof bowl wide
enough to sit over the saucepan. Add ½ teaspoon of the sweetener
and stir to mix well.

Put the honey, cinnamon, remaining sweetener, egg yolks, lemon zest
and juice into the bowl with the passion fruit mixture and whisk well
with an electric mixer. Set the bowl over the saucepan of simmering
water and continue to whisk for 15-20 minutes or until the mixture
is pale and thick and holds a trail when the beaters are lifted out.
Keep the water simmering gently – be careful not to let it bubble too
strongly or the eggs will cook and curdle.

Remove the bowl from the heat and continue to whisk for 2-3 minutes.

Divide the yogurt between four dessert glasses and top with the
zabaglione to serve.

*This dessert is even tastier after a bit of time in the
fridge so, if you can, make it in advance and chill
until you're ready to eat.*

ready in

20

minutes

desert island
fruit salad

serves 4

each serving is:

½ **Syn** on Extra Easy

½ **Syn** on Green

½ **Syn** on Original

2 kiwi fruits, peeled and
cut into bite-sized chunks

1 small papaya, peeled, seeded
and cut into bite-sized chunks

400g prepared pineapple chunks

1 banana, sliced

fresh mint sprigs, to decorate

fat free natural fromage frais,
to serve

for the syrup

3 tbsp pineapple juice

1cm piece of root ginger,
peeled and finely grated

juice and finely grated zest
of 1 lime

2 tsp sweetener

The chunky fruit in this unforgettable dish offers a taste of paradise, and the sensational syrup is sweet, warming and zesty all at once.

First make the syrup. Put the pineapple juice, ginger and lime juice in a small saucepan with 200ml of water and the sweetener. Stir well and bring to the boil. Remove from the heat and leave to cool.

Divide the fruit between bowls, pour over the syrup and toss to mix well. Scatter over the lime zest, decorate with mint sprigs and serve with fat free natural fromage frais.

orange blossom water and fig tartlets

serves 4

each serving is:

5 Syns on Extra Easy

5 Syns on Green

5 Syns on Original

100g ready-rolled puff pastry

100g fat free natural fromage frais

50g quark

1 tbsp finely grated orange zest, plus extra to decorate

½ tsp sweetener

1 tsp orange blossom water

4 figs, sliced into thin wedges

Fresh ripe figs are among the prettiest fruits around and these stunning creamy tarts show them off to perfection.

Preheat the oven to 220°C/Fan 200°C/Gas 7.

Line a baking sheet with baking parchment. Divide the pastry into four equal portions, roll each one into a square of about 10cm x 10cm and space them well apart on the prepared baking sheet.

With a sharp knife, score a border around the pastry, about 5mm in from the edge. Bake for 12-15 minutes or until the pastry is golden and has risen slightly. Remove from the oven and cool on wire racks.

Meanwhile, prepare the filling. Beat together the fromage frais, quark, orange zest, sweetener and orange blossom water.

Push down the centre of each tart, spoon in the filling and arrange the fig wedges on top. Dust lightly with icing sugar if you like (1 Syn per level teaspoon) and sprinkle over the extra orange zest to serve.

raspberry
meringues

Meringues usually take well over an hour but our super-speedy version cooks in less than 10 minutes – it's the ideal topping for deliciously sweet raspberries.

serves 4

each serving is:

2½ **Syns** on Extra Easy

2½ **Syns** on Green

2½ **Syns** on Original

Preheat the oven to 220°C/Fan 200°C/Gas 7.

Divide the sponge fingers between four heatproof ramekins.

Lightly crush the raspberries, stir in half of the sweetener and spread the mixture over the sponge fingers.

In a clean bowl, whisk the egg whites with the remaining sweetener until stiff and glossy. Spoon the mixture over the raspberries and bake for 8 minutes or until lightly golden.

Dust with icing sugar if you like (1 Syn per level teaspoon). These are best served hot.

4 sponge fingers,
roughly broken up

450g frozen raspberries, thawed

1 tbsp sweetener

3 egg whites

baked
fruit parcels

serves 4

each serving is:

4½ **Syns** on Extra Easy

4½ **Syns** on Green

4½ **Syns** on Original

---

4 plums, halved and stoned

4 apricots, halved and stoned

2 peaches, halved, stoned
and cut into wedges

100g blackberries

2 amaretti biscuits, crushed

½ tsp ground ginger

2 tsp soft brown sugar

fat free natural fromage frais,
to serve

It couldn't be easier to make this lovely fruit
dish – just wrap everything in tin foil and let
your oven do the rest.

Preheat the oven to 200°C/Fan 180°C/Gas 6.

Place the fruit, crushed biscuits, ginger and sugar in a bowl and mix
together carefully.

Cut out four large squares of tin foil. Divide the fruit mixture between
the foil squares, fold up to make little parcels and seal securely. Place
the parcels on a baking tray and bake for 15-20 minutes.

Spoon the fruit from each parcel on to plates and serve with a dollop
of fat free natural fromage frais.

tutti frutti
sorbet

Everyone will love this beautiful soft-scoop sorbet… and no one will guess it took less time to make than a cup of tea!

serves 4

each serving is:

4 Syns on Extra Easy

4 Syns on Green

4 Syns on Original

Put the frozen berries and bananas into a food processor or blender. Add the yogurt, sweetener and vanilla extract and blend for 1-2 minutes or until you have a ready-to-serve soft-scoop sorbet.

Serve in chilled dessert bowls, with your favourite fresh berries scattered over.

If you're not eating straight away, transfer the sorbet to a freezer-proof container and freeze until you're ready to serve.

400g frozen red berries

2 bananas, roughly chopped

175g pot Muller Light Cherry yogurt

2 tsp sweetener or to taste

1 tsp vanilla extract

fresh berries, to serve

tropical
eton mess

serves 4

each serving is:

1½ **Syns** on Extra Easy

1½ **Syns** on Green

1½ **Syns** on Original

6 passion fruits

1 tsp sweetener

400g prepared pineapple chunks

1 large banana, sliced

1 small papaya, peeled, seeded and cut into bite-sized chunks

175g pot Muller Light Vanilla yogurt

2 meringue nests, roughly crushed

The original version of this sweet treat has been served at the famous public school since the 19th century and our exotic twist brings it right up to date.

Put the pulp and seeds from the passion fruits in a small saucepan with the sweetener and 75ml of water. Heat gently for 2-3 minutes until the sweetener has dissolved then stir to mix well. Remove from the heat and set aside to cool.

Meanwhile, put the rest of the fruit into a large bowl, add the yogurt and half the passion fruit mixture and swirl through.

Fold in the meringue and divide the mixture between four chilled dessert glasses. Spoon over the remaining passion fruit mixture to serve.

ready in

20
minutes

cherry-berry
semolina pots

serves 4

each serving is:

4 Syns on Extra Easy

4 Syns on Green

4 Syns on Original

50g dried semolina

400ml skimmed milk

¼ tsp crushed cardamom seeds

2 tsp sweetener

1 tbsp finely grated orange zest, plus extra to decorate

300g mixed berries

100g cherries, to decorate

If semolina conjures up memories of school dinners, think again! These gorgeous individual pots are filled with hidden fruity treasure for everyone to discover.

Place the semolina in a saucepan and whisk in 100ml of water, the milk and cardamom seeds. Bring to the boil over a medium heat, stirring continuously. This should take about 6-8 minutes. Turn the heat down to low and simmer for 5-6 minutes, stirring, until the semolina is thick, creamy and smooth.

Remove the pan from the heat and stir in the sweetener and orange zest. Add most of the mixed berries and fold them through gently.

Divide the mixture between four tea-cups or bowls and serve warm, decorated with the cherries, remaining berries and extra orange zest.

banana, rum
and nectarine sauté

serves 4

each serving is:

4½ **Syns** on Extra Easy

4½ **Syns** on Green

4½ **Syns** on Original

low calorie cooking spray

2 bananas, thickly sliced diagonally

3 nectarines, halved,
stoned and cut into wedges

1-2 tsp sweetener, to taste

finely grated zest
and juice of 1 orange

1 tbsp dark rum

1 tsp ground cinnamon

fat free natural fromage frais,
to serve

fresh mint leaves, to decorate

Who can resist golden, sautéed fruit with a hint
of cinnamon and a wicked splash of rum?
It's the essence of the Caribbean in a bowl!

Spray a large non-stick frying pan with low calorie cooking spray and
place over a medium-high heat. Add the bananas and nectarines and
stir-fry for 2-3 minutes or until just softened.

Stir in the sweetener, orange zest and juice, rum and cinnamon and
stir-fry for 1-2 minutes.

Remove from the heat and serve hot with a dollop of fromage frais
and mint leaves scattered over.

spiced berries with cinnamon cream

Mouth-watering fresh berries speak for themselves in this no-fuss dessert served with cinnamon-scented fromage frais.

Put all the fruit in a serving bowl and sprinkle over the sweetener, black pepper and lemon juice. Toss to mix well.

Mix together all the ingredients for the cinnamon cream and serve with the spiced berries.

serves 4

each serving is:

Free on Extra Easy

Free on Green

Free on Original

200g blueberries

200g raspberries

400g strawberries, hulled and quartered

¼ tsp sweetener

¼ tsp freshly ground black pepper

juice of 1 lemon

for the cinnamon cream

200g fat free natural fromage frais

¼ tsp sweetener

¼ tsp ground cinnamon

ready in

30

minutes

spiced
melon medley

serves 4

each serving is:

Free on Extra Easy

Free on Green

Free on Original

---

1 ripe honeydew melon, halved and seeded

1 ripe cantaloupe melon, halved and seeded

½ small watermelon, seeded

fat free natural fromage frais or yogurt, to serve

for the syrup

1 tbsp sweetener

¼ tsp crushed cardamom seeds

1 cinnamon stick

finely grated zest of ½ orange

Melon balls bursting with freshness are drizzled with a delicately spiced syrup in this simple dish – and it's completely Free!

First make the syrup. Put the sweetener, cardamom seeds, cinnamon stick, orange zest and 250ml of water in a small saucepan and bring to the boil. Reduce the heat to low and simmer gently for 10 minutes.

Meanwhile, use a melon baller to make balls from the melons and watermelon and divide them between bowls. (If you don't have a melon baller, just dice the fruit.)

Remove the syrup from the heat, discard the cinnamon stick and allow to cool. Spoon the syrup over the fruit and serve with a dollop of fat free natural fromage frais or yogurt.

orchard fruit trifles

It's hard to say no to a trifle, especially as these beauties are a celebration of the British countryside!

Roughly break up the sponge fingers and divide between four dessert glasses.

Mix together the fruit and add to the glasses.

Spoon the custard over the fruit, top with the fromage frais and decorate with mint sprigs to serve.

For an even quicker trifle, replace the fruit with 450g mixed berries.

serves 4

each serving is:

3 Syns on Extra Easy

3 Syns on Green

3 Syns on Original

2 sponge fingers

2 red apples, halved, cored and roughly chopped

2 ripe pears, halved, cored and roughly chopped

4 plums, halved, stoned and roughly chopped

200g low fat custard

200g fat free natural fromage frais

fresh mint sprigs, to decorate

chocolate brandy pots

ready in
20
minutes

serves 4

each serving is:

5 Syns on Extra Easy

5 Syns on Green

5 Syns on Original

70g dark chocolate, roughly chopped

350g quark

2 tbsp sweetener

1 tsp brandy

1 tsp vanilla extract

175g pot Muller Light Vanilla yogurt

4 cherries

Soft, creamy quark is fantastic blended with rich, dark chocolate and a luxurious dash of brandy in this indulgent dessert.

Place the chocolate in a heatproof bowl over a saucepan of lightly simmering water and heat for 8-10 minutes or until melted, taking care that the base of the bowl does not touch the water.

Put the quark in a blender or food processor with the sweetener, brandy and vanilla extract. Scrape in the melted chocolate and blend until smooth.

Transfer this mixture into four small dessert glasses or ramekins, spoon over the vanilla yogurt and top with a cherry.

These are delicious served with a dusting of cocoa powder (½ Syn per level teaspoon) and icing sugar (1 Syn per level teaspoon).

These chocolate pots are even tastier after a bit of time in the fridge so, if you can, make them in advance and chill until you're ready to eat.

index

First published in 2014 by
Slimming World
Clover Nook Road
Somercotes
Alfreton
Derbyshire
DE55 4SW
UK
www.slimmingworld.com

Created and designed by
Slimming World's publications team.
Publications manager: Allison Brentnall
Editor: Oliver Maxey
Designers: Kathryn Briggs and Fabiana Viracca-Butler
Syn calculation: Carole Lamb

Recipes and food styling: Sunil Vijayakar
Photographs: Gareth Morgans
Styling: Morag Farquhar

Front cover photograph:
Speedy chicken jambalaya, page 80

Back cover photographs, from left:
Steak au poivre with sautéed potatoes, page 18
Honey and mustard salmon, page 132
Courgette ribbon pasta, page 182
Chocolate brandy pots, page 224

did you know?

10p from the sale of this book goes to our charitable foundation SMILES (Slimmers Making it a Little Easier for Someone), whose charity partners have included the NSPCC, Barnardo's, Cancer Research UK and the Marie Keating Foundation. In 2014 we donated £125,000 from book sales.